The **WYNNS** Fleet

120 Years of Road Haulage

by Paul Heaton

P.M. Heaton Publishing
Abergavenny Monmouthshire
Great Britain
2003

Front cover: Superior she certainly is. The new and as yet unregistered Scammell Contractor Mk2 - 250ton drawbar tractor. Delivered in 1977 it was the main attraction on the Leyland Special Vehicles Stand at the Commercial Motor Show at Earls Court. This vehicle was registered as RWO73R (fleet no: 602). Passing from Robert Wynn & Sons Ltd., Newport in 1982 it went to Wynns Heavy Haulage, Stafford, thence United Heavy Transport and Econofreight United Heavy Haulage, and is now owned and preserved by Robert Willson, Pontypool.

Title page: Pictured in 1880 some of the horses and carts employed by WYNNS. At that time seventeen year old Robert Wynn lived at home with his widowed mother at No. 4, Station Street, Newport, whilst business was conducted from a yard at No. 30, Shaftesbury Street.

Back cover: Fowler Steam Road Locomotive DW2121 participating in Newport Carnival, and Heralding the new Millennium. Two Diamond T drawbar tractors, EDW95 (160) and ODW 937 (262) negotiate Hardwick Roundabout, Abergavenny enroute to Abergavenny Steam Rally at Whitsun. Both in preservation they are owned by Howard Francis of Ewyas Harold and Steve Roberts of Cwmbran, respectively.

*Dedicated to all those who spent
their working lives with Wynns
and helped make this story*

ISBN 1 872006 15 9

(c) First Edition October, 2003
P.M. Heaton

Published by P. M. Heaton Publishing
Abergavenny, Monmouthshire, NP7 8NG

Printed in Great Britain by
The Amadeus Press Ltd.,
Cleckheaton, West Yorkshire, BD19 4TQ

WYNNS

The renowned haulage business of Robert Wynn & Sons was founded at Newport in 1863 when Thomas Wynn, then 42 years old, acquired a pair of horses and a cart and commenced undertaking deliveries in and around the town. Trade quickly expanded and the horse gave way to steam and then to petrol and diesel engined vehicles of ever increasing size. Surviving for 120 years, the firm was unusual in that it specialised in a number of core activities - local deliveries in South Wales, timber extraction, heavy haulage throughout the United Kingdom and abroad, a London nightly trunk service, land reclamation and tippers, tankers and mobile cranes, and specialised in seating heavy equipment and machinery on site.

Although WYNNS disappeared twenty years ago, it is well remembered far and wide, due in no small part by the enterprise shown by four generations of the same family and the loyal service given by many employees who often spent their entire working lives with the firm. WYNNS has become something of a cult, and many of their former vehicles have found a place in history through preservation.

Since compiling and publishing the books WYNNS - The First 100 Years (1995) and WYNNS - The Last 20 Years (1996) and having laid out the first draft of WYNNS Overseas (1998) I have been inundated by requests to write a more comprehensive volume devoted to the WYNNS fleet and I hope that readers will think I have achieved this in these pages. However, I doubt that a full and accurate list of the fleet could ever be achieved, but I would welcome information from anyone who could add to that already known.

The one person who has done the most to ensure WYNNS is never forgotten must surely be John Harrington, and I would like to pay particular tribute to him for the decades of research he has undertaken. Having spent months delving through hundreds of thousands of vehicle registration documents I know the effort required. I would like to thank all those who have helped with information and photographs, as follows: Roger Banfield, Graham Booth, John Fletcher, Howard Francis, Paul Hancox, Granville Hollister, Robert Price, R.A. Whitehead, Alan Williams, Joseph Willson, Robert Willson and a particular thanks to the Curator and staff at the Gwent Record Office.

Paul Heaton
Abergavenny

October, 2003

Robert Wynn (fourth from the left) is shown in front of a tank locomotive
carried on a trailer drawn by a team of six horses c1900.

*Half page advert which appeared in the 1898 edition of Johns Newport Almanac.
At the time Robert Wynn was trading from 30, Shaftesbury Street, and living at
42, Maindee Parade. The other advert on the page, of Clarke's of
Griffin Street, is included as also being of interest.*

4

Two views of a filter being delivered to Pant-yr-eos Reservoir for Newport Corporation in 1908. In the upper picture, Robert Wynn waistcoated and with sleeves rolled up is seen standing against the Burrell Road Locomotive AX183 which he had bought new in August, 1906. This was the first vehicle registered by WYNNS. The other vehicle is believed to be the unregistered Wallis-Stevens steamer acquired in July, 1905.

Motor Car Acts, 1896 and 1903,
and
Regulations of Local Government Board,
19th November, 1903, and
27th December, 1904.

REGISTER OF HEAVY

Index Mark and Number on Identification Plates. (1)	Full Name of Owner, and Postal Address of his usual Residence. (2)	Description or Type of Car. (3)	Type and Colour of Body of Car. (4)	Weight Unladen. (5)	Axle-weight of each Axle. (6)
A B 130	Parkinson & Chapman, Wainfelin, Pontypool	Light Locomotive Steam. 3 h.p. "No 2578"	Traction Engine Body. Green.	2 tons 16 cwt 3 qrs	Front: 1 ton 3c Rear: 2 tons 9c
A X 179	Abraham Wyke Harrison. Monmouth Road Abergavenny	5 ton Straker Steam Wagon	Brown with name written on	4 tons 1 cwt	Front: 1 ton 1 Rear: 2 tons 1
A X 183	Robert Wynn Shaftesbury Road Newport, Mon.	Steam Tractor Makers:- Chas. Burrell & Sons, Ltd. Thetford Norfolk	Body painted lake	4 tons 19 cwt 2 qrs	Front: 1 ton 5 c Rear: 3 14
A X 225	S A Bees & Co (Cardiff) Ld. 7, Mount Stuart Square, Cardiff	Straker & Squire's Steam Motor Wagon	Van body, painted green	4 tons 19 cwt	Front: 2 tons Rear: 2

Motor Car Acts, 1896 and 1903,
and
Regulations of Local Government Board,
19th November, 1903, and
27th December, 1904.

REGISTER OF HEAVY M

Index Mark and Number on Identification Plates. (1)	Full Name of Owner, and Postal Address of his usual Residence. (2)	Description or Type of Car. (3)	Type and Colour of Body of Car. (4)	Weight Unladen. (5)	Axle-weight of each Axle. (6)
A X 183	James Graven, Engineering Works, Ely Cambs.	Steam Tractor Makers:- Chas. Burrell & Sons, Ltd. Thetford Norfolk	Body painted Lake	4 tons 19 cwt 2 qrs.	Front: 1 ton 5 cwt 2 Rear: 3 - 14 - 0
A X 183	C R N Selleck, for The Dartmoor China Clay Co. Ltd., Shaugh Roborough R.S.O. Devon	Steam Tractor. Makers:- Chas. Burrell & Son, Ltd. Thetford Norfolk	Body painted Lake	4 tons. 19 cwt 2 qrs.	Front: 1 ton 5 cwt Rear: 3 - 14 -
A X 572	Thomas Francis Edwards, Whitelye Farm. Tintern.	4 h.p. Steam Tractor Makers:- Foster, Lincoln	Body painted Lake	4 tons 15 cwt	Front: 2 tons Rear: 4 tons 15
A X 683	Blackwood (Mon) Motor Co. Ltd. C.F. Adams, Secretary, High Street Chambers, Blackwood	30 h.p. Daimler	Char-a-banc Grey	3 tons 6 cwt.	Front: 1 ton 18 Rear: 2 tons 1

CARS.

Motor Act, M 2. Shaw & Sons, Fetter Lane, E.C. (87083n)

meter of Wheels. (7)	Width and Material of Tires. (8)	Maximum Speed permissible. (9)	Whether intended for (10)			Date of Registration. (11)	If Cancelled, Date of Cancellation. (12)
			(a) Private Use.	(b) Use for Trade Purposes.	(c) Use as a Public Conveyance.		
t: 3 ft. 4 ft.	Front :- 4½° Rear : 8½°	5 miles an hour		Yes.		10th October, 1905.	
t: 2ft 7ins 3 ft. 6ins	Iron Tires Front 5 inches Rear 7 inches	5 miles an hour		Yes		22nd June, 1906	Transferred p. 14.
t: 3 ft. 5 ft.	Front : 5 in wide Rear : 8 in wide	Five miles an hour.		Yes		11th August 1906	Transferred p. 7
ng Wheels: 6" × 10" d. Wheels 8" × 5"	Cast Steel Road wheels Driving wheels 10" on face	Five miles an hour		Yes.		6th May 1907	

CARS.

Motor Act, M 2. Shaw & Sons, Fetter Lane, E.C. (87083n)

meter of Wheels. (7)	Width and Material of Tires. (8)	Maximum Speed permissible. (9)	Whether intended for (10)			Date of Registration. (11)	If Cancelled, Date of Cancellation. (12)
			(a) Private Use.	(b) Use for Trade Purposes.	(c) Use as a Public Conveyance.		
3ft 5ft	Front : 5" Rear : 8" Iron	5 mi. per hour.		Yes		23rd July, 1913.	T. see p. 2 Transferred see below
3ft 5ft	Front : 5" Rear : 8" Iron	5 mi. per hour.		Yes		16th August, 1913.	T. see above
3' 2" 5' 2"	12" Iron	5 mi. per hour.		Yes		3rd September 1913.	
"	5 " Rubber	12 mi. per hour.		Yes		29th May 1914.	✓

Reproduced are entries from pages 2 and 7 of the Monmouthshire County Council Register of Heavy Motor Cars, showing the registration of Robert Wynn's Burrell steam tractor AX183 dated August 11, 1906. This was the seventh goods vehicle to be registered by the authority, and holds the distinction of being the first ever vehicle licensed by Robert Wynn. Also reproduced are the entries referring to the vehicle's subsequent sale on July 22, 1913 and again on August 16, 1913. (Courtesy of Gwent Record Office).

Index No.	Fleet No.	Vehicle.	Date Aqd.	Notes.
		Burrell Showman's Steam engine	1905	Origins unknown, unregistered;c1919 to E. Danter, Newport; 1920s to Messrs Drakeley, Birmingham who registered vehicle as OH4747
		Wallis-Stevens 5ton Road Locomotive	7.1905	Unregistered; no other details
AX183		Burrell 5ton Road Locomotive	11.8.1906	ULW 4t 19c 2q; 22.7.1913 to James Graven,Ely, Cambs.; 16.8.1913 to Dartmoor China Clay Company, Roborough, Devon
BJ1103		Garrett 5ton Road Locomotive	24.8.1910	Works No: 28733; 1921 sold
DW27		RAC 15.8hp motor car	11.4.1914	Number re-issued on 1.2.1921; see below
DW999		Palladium 25hp motor lorry	15.6.1916	ULW 2tons
DW4		Karrier 50hp flat bed motor lorry	25.6.1919	ULW 3t 19c; re-issued number
M6621		Foden 5ton 4wl steam wagon	c1914	New in 6.1914; owned by Williams, Llanwern 9.1919
KT2682		Aveling Porter 5ton steam wagon	c1914	Bought from A.S. Morgan when almost new; c1916 to Leicester & Warwick Power Supply Company
DW1176		Tyler motor lorry	11.2.1919	ULW 3tons
DW494		Premier 2.5hp motor cycle	24.3.1919	Weight 100lbs; bought secondhand
DW369		Triumph 4hp motor cycle	23.9.1919	Weight 240lbs; re-issued number
DW1529		Pagefield 40hp motor lorry	15.3.1920	ULW 3t 5c.
DW2119	2	Garrett 5ton Road Locomotive	26.1.1921	ULW 7t 2c 2q; Works No: 32703; Delivered new to Alban Thomas, Caerleon on 20.5.1915; original number BJ2562
DW2120		Burrell 5ton Road Locomotive	26.1.1921	ULW 12t 10c; built in 12.1915, bought secondhand; 1920s to G. Rogers, Chipping Sodbury; still survived in the 1960's
DW2121	3	Fowler 5ton Road Locomotive	26.1.1921	ULW 13t 5c; bought new ex-works in 1920; preserved by WYNNS and in 1980 on loan to Tredegar House, Newport; 1994 to John Griffiths, Nelson; 2000 to owner based in Cornwall
DW27		Vulcan 15.7hp touring car	1.2.1921	Re-issued number

Index No.	Fleet No.	Vehicle.	Date Aqd.	Notes.
DW2286		Burrell Road Locomotive	24.4.1921	ULW 10t 18c; no other details
DW788		Ford van	30.5.1921	Bought second hand
DW526		Peerless motor lorry	6.1921	Re-issued number
DW583		Minerva 3.5hp motor cycle	c1921	Weight 125lbs; bought secondhand
DW488		Ford lorry	30.6.1921	ULW 17cwt; re-issued number
DW2464		Triumph 4hp motor cycle	23.7.1921	Weight 250lbs
DW2844		Albion motor lorry	4.9.1922	ULW 2t 7c 2q.
DW532		Peerless motor lorry	7.12.1922	Re-issued number
DW3065		Peerless motor lorry	10.4.1923	ULW 3t 14c.
BJ4386		Garrett 5ton 4wl steam wagon	1921	Works No: 33597; new on 7.7.1919 to W. Powell, Bridgend
M7988		Foden 5ton 4wl steam wagon	1921	New in 1915; bought from Mrs. E. Lawson, Hilston Park, Skenfrith; 1924 disposed of
DW392		Rudge 3.5hp motor cycle	20.10.1923	Weight about 200lbs; new in 1914; bought secondhand
DW811		Rover motor car	2.8.1923	Re-issued number
DW3636		Peerless motor lorry	5.1924	
DW3796		Peerless motor lorry	5.1924	
DW3828		Private motor car	7.1924	Make unknown
DW3444		AEC motor lorry	8.3.1924	Bought from Venn & McPherson, Newport
DW3445		Fiat motor lorry	8.3.1924	Bought from Venn & McPherson, Newport
DW3446		Pierce Arrow motor lorry	8.3.1924	Bought from Venn & McPherson, Newport
DW3447		Pierce Arrow motor lorry	8.3.1924	Bought from Venn & McPherson, Newport
DW3924		Morris Cowley motor car	24.12.1924	
BJ4786		Garrett Super 4wl steam wagon	1924	Works No: 33720; new on 28.11.1919 to Avana Flour Mills, Cardiff
BJ5518		Garrett Super 4wl steam wagon	1924	Works No: 33942; new on 16.9.1920 to Avana Flour Mills, Cardiff

Two Road Locomotives hauling three narrow gauge contractors locomotives from Newport to Llanvihangel Crucorney during the building of the Black Mountains Reservoir for the Abertillery & District Water Supply Board. The leading vehicle is the Garrett DW2119 new in May, 1915 to Alban Thomas of Caerleon and acquired by WYNNS in 1921. The other steamer is the Fowler DW2121 dating from 1920 and registered in January, 1921.

(Above): The Fowler steam road locomotive DW2121 is shown at Liswerry Sidings before setting out for Newport Power Station with an electric stator weighing 36 tons.

(Below): Boxed machinery being collected at Newport Docks. DW2121 and DW2119 being used with a variety of solid tyred trailers.

(Above): Believed to be the Burrell Road Locomotive DW2286 shown drawing a gun barrell following the First World War on the 40ton capacity boiler wagon which had been built by the firm in 1890.
This trailer survives today in preservation.

(Below): DW2121 survives today, but is seen here leading Newport Carnival in the late 1970s.

Three WYNNS motor lorries: Peerless DW526 (acquired in 1921), Albion DW2844 (1922) and Karrier DW4 (1919) pictured at the firm's yard at 50, Shaftesbury Street, Newport, where they had moved in 1902.

This Chevrolet drawbar tractor, index number DW5608 (67) was used on heavy haulage.
Supplied in July, 1927 by Atlas Garages, Newport, note the vehicles very short wheelbase.

Bought by the WYNNS owned company - Pearce Haulage in 1933, this Scammell UW167 dating from 1930 was rebuilt as a timber tractor to a patented design of H.P. Wynn. After lying idle for many years it was bought recently by John Harrington who is in course of restoring it.

Used on local deliveries, this Daimler dropside motor lorry HM1507 (43) was bought secondhand c1929.

15

Index No.	Fleet No.	Vehicle.	Date Aqd.	Notes.
MA744		Foden 3ton steam wagon	1925	New in 1919; bought from T.E. Cunliffe Birmingham; 4.1929 disposed of.
DW3938		Fiat motor lorry	3.1.1925	
DW4012		AEC motor lorry	2.3.1925	
DW4020		AEC motor lorry	5.2.1925	
DW4040		Foden articulated steam lorry	16.3.1925	
DW4339		AEC motor lorry	10.6.1925	
DW4469		Peerless motor lorry	18.7.1925	
DW4640	25	Foden 4ton steam lorry	11.1925	
DW4751		AEC motor lorry	9.3.1926	
DW5276		AEC motor lorry	25.2.1927	
DW5608	67	Chevrolet drawbar tractor	12.7.1927	Supplied new by Atlas Garages, Newport
DW5718		Scammell articulated lorry	19.10.1927	WYNNS first Scammell
UX3240		Sentinel 6wl steam wagon	1927	New in 1926, supplied ex-works, possibly a demonstrator; sold by 1931
YI8056		Sentinel 4wl steam wagon	1927	New in 1925; bought from Williams & Woods, Dublin; subsequently ran for Crosse & Blackwell
NT3211		Sentinel 4wl steam wagon	1927	New in 1923; bought from Llewellyn, Ross on Wye; ran until 6.1948
DW6059		AEC motor lorry	5.1928	
DW6060	38	Garrett 6wl steam wagon	29.5.1928	Works No: 35156; originally a Garrett demonstrator number RT4342 dating from 4.1928; bought by WYNNS and re-registered; in 1929 returned to Garretts and part exchanged for DW6616 (Works No: 35315) see later; vehicle was rebuilt as a side tipper and used as a demonstrator; 15.5.1931 to Maynard & Sons, Crawley Down, Sussex
AX6966	37	Sentinel steam wagon	1928	New in 1.1925 to Willerbey Harvey & Co. Ltd., 50, Cross Street, Abergavenny
DW6350		Leyland motor lorry	1928	
DW6404		Chevrolet motor lorry	1928	May have been similar to DW5608
DW6440	25	Sentinel articulated steam lorry	3.1929	

16

Index No.	Fleet No.	Vehicle.	Date Aqd.	Notes.
UH5427		Sentinel steam lorry	c1929	New in 1928 to Spillers, Cardiff
DW6615		Daimler motor lorry	1929	Re-conditioned vehicle
DW6616	42	Garrett 6wl steam wagon	6.7.1929	Works No: 35315; replaced DW6060
HM1507	43	Daimler motor lorry	c1929	Bought second hand from London owners
DW6681		Sentinel steam lorry	1929	Owned by Pearce Haulage Co.; this business was taken over by WYNNS in 1930, and remained registered owners of some vehicles until 1947
DW6750		Sentinel steam lorry	1929	Owned by Pearce Haulage Co.; see DW6681 above
DW6887		Garrett 5ton Road Locomotive	13.2.1930	Works No: 33648; when built was intended for J.Davies, Redmarley, Glos. but was sold new ex-works to F. Munn, Cardiff as BJ4521 on 17.10.1919; later passing to Cardiff Corporation from whom WYNNS bought and re-registered vehicle
UW7399		Scammell 15ton articulated lorry	12.1930	New in 12.1929; believed to be a Demonstrator
OT3478		Sentinel 4wl tipper	1930	New in 1929, bought from Hampshire operator
DW7121		Leyland motor lorry	13.2.1930	Sold to Scammell in 1.1932, believed as part-payment
WO2936	48	AEC lorry	2.1930	Rebuilt by WYNNS from a salvaged bus chassis, originally owned by Lewis & James, Cross Keys
DW7244		AEC motor lorry	11.1930	Supplied by Romilly Motors, Cardiff
DW7260		AEC motor lorry	12.1930	Supplied by Romilly Motors, Cardiff
DW7261		AEC motor lorry	12.1930	Supplied by Romilly Motors, Cardiff
DW7333		Austin motor car	1931	Supplied by Jones Newport Garage
DW7487		Bedford motor lorry	2.6.1931	Supplied by Atlas Garages, Newport; WYNNS first Bedford lorry
DW7652	52	Scammell 6wl motor lorry	17.11.1931	Acquired for the London night trunk service
DW7653	53	Scammell 6wl motor lorry	17.11.1931	Acquired for the London night trunk service
DW7671	6	Scammell motor lorry	1931	Supplied reconditioned ex-works owned by Pearce Haulage Co. (1930) Ltd

In 1928 WYNNS took delivery of a 6-wheel steam wagon from Garretts at Leiston. With permission of R.A. Whitehead I quote from his book Garrett Wagons Part 2 Undertypes (1994):

The first production (6-wheeler) was a non-tipper, No.35156, finished in March, 1928, and licensed on April 3. For two months it was paraded round potential purchasers, mostly firms who had already showed interest in response to salesman's visits, at the end of which it was sold to Robert Wynn & Sons Ltd., at Newport, Monmouthshire. It did not have a happy career with them - and - in the case of the wagon sold in June, 1928, to Robert Wynn in Newport, problems had developed in the gears, and with the square section of the crankshaft upon which the crankshaft gears were mounted. Matters so deteriorated with the Wynns wagon that in the Spring of 1929 the firm was persuaded, or coerced, into taking it back in exchange for a new wagon, No. 35315, for which they received a token payment of £175.

(Pictured left): Seen in the Tower Works of Garretts at Leiston, Norfolk, is a rear end chassis view of the first production 6-wheeler

The same vehicle still in primer
standing outside Garretts erecting shop.

Used initially as a demonstrator the vehicle which first bore the number RT4342, was re-registered at Newport as DW6060 (Fleet No: 38) on May 29,1928, although Garrett's records show the sale as taking place on June 12. It is shown in Victory Road, Leiston, prior to handing over to WYNNS. Incidentally the vehicle which replaced it the following year was DW6616 (42).

Robert Wynn & Sons Ltd advert in the 1930 edition of Kelly's Directory of Newport.
The vehicle illustrated is the Foden articulated steam lorry DW4040 dating from March, 1925.
The firm was expanding rapidly, with offices at Newport, Cardiff and London, but still advertised the use
of horses as well as petrol engined and steam driven vehicles.

Bought new in 1931 these Scammell 6-wheel lorries DW7652 (52) and DW7653 (53)
were used on the London nightly trunk service.

Another pair of Scammell 6 wheelers were bought in October, 1933,
they were DW8424 (10) and DW 8425 (11) - illustrated.

Index No.	Fleet No.	Vehicle.	Date Aqd.	Notes.
DW7672	8	Scammell motor lorry	1931	Supplied reconditioned ex-works owned by Pearce Haulage Co. (1930) Ltd
DW7692		Standard motor car	1931	
BO6586	57	Sentinel steam lorry	c1931	New in 1923, bought second hand
DW8424	10	Scammell 6wl motor lorry	10.1933	Acquired for the London night trunk service
DW8425	11	Scammell 6wl motor lorry	10.1933	Acquired for the London night trunk service
UW167	12	Scammell timber tractor	1933	New in 1930 to W.E. Clarke, London; bought by Pearce Haulage Co. and rebuilt as a timber tractor to a patented design of H.P. Wynn; for many years lay at Phillips Garage, Bassaleg; 1998 acquired by John Harrington, London; preserved and in course of restoration
VT1090		Scammell 6wl motor lorry	1933	New in 3.1928 to Beresford Transport, Stoke-on-Trent; owned by Pearce Haulage Co.; used on the London night trunk service
YF9715		Scammell motor lorry	1933	New in 4.1927; bought by Pearce Haulage Co.
KH9895	51	Scammell 45ton articulated tractor unit	1933	New in 11.1929 to G. Earle, Hull fitted with solid tyres; this vehicle was an important part of WYNNS heavy haulage fleet prior to and during the Second World War; subsequently sold to Whayman, Pontypridd and broken up in 1963.
GW1477	70	Scammell 4wl motor lorry	2.1933	Earlier origins unknown; bought damaged and rebuilt; burnt out and destroyed on the London night trunk service
WO323	60	Sentinel steam timber tractor	1933	New to Williams Bros., Pandy on 2.5.1927; rebuilt by WYNNS following an accident at Brecon
WO1072		Sentinel steam timber tractor	1933	New to Williams Bros., Pandy on 1.11.1927
WO5737	59	Sentinel steam timber tractor	1933	New to Williams Bros., Pandy on 26.9.1931; In 1935 to N. Woollaston, Shirley, Warks.
WO5870	31	Foden steam timber tractor	1933	New to Hire Purchase Securities Ltd., Kyle, Bridgend in 1931; had been based at Portskewitt Sawmills

Index No.	Fleet No.	Vehicle.	Date Aqd.	Notes.
UH5757	64	Chevrolet motor lorry	1933	Bought secondhand, origins unknown
	65	Chevrolet 6wl motor lorry	1933	Details unknown; disposed of by 1948
	66	Chevrolet 6wl motor lorry	1933	Details unknown; disposed of by 1948
	71	Scammell 6wl motor lorry	1933	Demonstrator, details unknown
	72	Leyland motor van	1933	Bought from Pan Products, Dock Street, Newport - an important customer; no other details
DW8587	75	Sentinel 4wl steam lorry	2.1934	Acquired for the London night trunk service; sometimes used with a drawbar trailer
DW8588	76	Sentinel 4wl steam lorry	2.1934	Details as for DW8587
DW8631	77	Garner 6wl motor lorry	3.1934	
DW8632	78	Garner 6wl motor lorry	3.1934	
DW8633	79	Garner 6wl motor lorry	4.1934	
DW8634	80	Garner 6wl motor lorry	5.1934	
LG571		Sentinel 4wl steam wagon	1934	New in 1929, other details unknown; 1934 to Messrs Simmons, Leighton Buzzard
UX9771	73	Sentinel 6wl steam lorry	1934	New in 1932, bought from Penarth Brickworks
UX8686		Sentinel 6wl steam lorry	1934	New in 1931, bought from Davies Bros., Llandeilo; 10.1943 out of service
DW9466		Scammell articulated tractor unit	7.1935	Reconditioned vehicle
DW9540		Bedford 5ton flat motor lorry	8.1935	Supplied by Atlas Garages, Newport
DW9541		Bedford 5ton flat motor lorry	9.1935	Supplied by Atlas Garages, Newport
DW9642	74	Leyland motor lorry	11.1935	
	22	Scammell articulated motor lorry	1935	Origins unknown; used on a contract to Sharps Toffees with a van trailer.
DW9726	27	Bedford articulated motor lorry	1.1936	Supplied by Atlas Garages, Newport
DW9727	28	Bedford 3ton flat motor lorry	12.1935	Supplied by Atlas Garages, Newport
DW9728	29	Bedford 3ton flat motor lorry	12.1935	Supplied by Atlas Garages, Newport
DW9735	35	Scammell timber tractor	12.1935	Re-constructed vehicle
DW9736		Leyland motor lorry	2.1936	Re-constructed vehicle
DW9754		Bedford motor lorry	2.1936	Supplied by Atlas Garages, Newport

Bought in 1933 from G. Earle of Hull this Scammell articulated tractor unit KH9895 (51) was fitted with solid tyres. It was an important pre-war unit of the heavy haulage fleet. It is shown in Winter weather loaded with an excavator, note the coat draped over the radiator.

Another view of KH9895 hard at work

This view taken from the London Evening News of July, 3, 1943, shows the Scammell KH9895 (51)
drawing a landing craft. This photograph was designed to deceive the enemy.

DW8588 (76) and DW8587 (75) - two Sentinel 4 wheel steam
wagons bought in 1934 for the London Trunk.

Sentinel steam wagon, index no: DW8588 is shown operating on heavy haulage.
The load is a 20ton - 50ft Air Receiver enroute from Wolverhampton to Seven Sisters, Glamorgan.

Delivered between March and May, 1934, these four Garner 6-wheel lorries DW8631-DW8634
were used on daily services throughout South Wales.

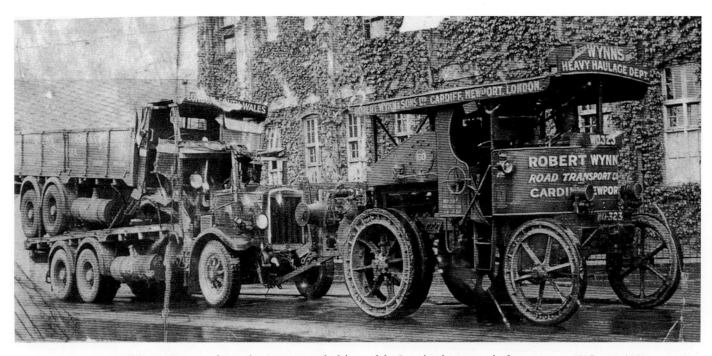

New to Williams Bros., of Pandy, Monmouthshire, this Sentinel steam timber tractor WO323 (60)
was one of three such vehicles bought in 1933 from this operator.

Two views of a rebuilt and re-registered Scammell timber tractor DW9735 (35) operating on the extraction of round timber. It should not be underestimated how important this business was to the fortunes of the firm.

Index No.	Fleet No.	Vehicle.	Date Aqd.	Notes.
DW9852	49	Scammell timber tractor	2.1936	Re-constructed vehicle
ADW110		Oldsmobile motor car	5.1936	
ADW401		Dodge tipper	12.1936	Supplied by Morse Motors, Cardiff
ADW402		Dodge tipper	12.1936	Supplied by Morse Motors, Cardiff
ADW403		Dodge articulated tractor unit	11.1936	Supplied by Morse Motors, Cardiff
ADW616	16	Scammell timber tractor	3.1937	
ADW617	81	Scammell 8wl flat motor lorry	5.1937	Acquired for the London night trunk service; later converted to a tanker
ADW770		Morris 20hp motor lorry	4.1937	Assembled by WYNNS from parts
ADW862		Latil timber tractor	5.1937	
BDW82	82	Scammell 50ton articulated tractor unit	9.1937	
UU3818	85	Scammell articulated tractor unit	12.1937	New in 1929; bought from Shell Mex
	4	Maudslay tipper	1937	Details not known
	5	Maudslay tipper	1937	Details not known
BDW394	84	Caterpillar tractor	2.1938	Tracked vehicle for timber extraction
UL6788	86	Scammell articulated tractor unit	4.1938	New in 4.1929; bought from Shell Mex
BDW721		Bedford 5ton flat lorry	6.1938	Supplied by Atlas Garages, Newport; 1951 to British Road Services
BDW722		Bedford tipper	6.1938	Supplied by Atlas Garages, Newport
BDW723		Bedford motor lorry	9.1938	Doubt if this vehicle existed, as number re-allocated to a Ford 8 motor car for Newport Mon. Motor Company
BDW798		Bedford tipper	8.1938	Supplied by Atlas Garages, Newport
BDW957	88	Bedford tipper	10.1938	
CDW33	87	Scammell 45ton articulated tractor unit	11.1938	Originally with solid rear tyres; later operated as a drawbar tractor
	48	Commer lorry	c1938	No details
	38	Dennis 6wl lorry	c1938	No details
		Dennis 4wl lorry	c1938	No details
		Dennis 4wl lorry	c1938	No details
		Caterpillar tractor	c1939	Bought second hand; tracked vehicle for timber extraction

Index No.	Fleet No.	Vehicle.	Date Aqd.	Notes.
		Caterpillar tractor	c1939	Bought second hand; tracked vehicle for timber extraction
		Latil timber tractor	c1939	No details
		Latil timber tractor	c1939	No details
YS1474		Scammell 4wl lorry	c1939	Believed bought for spares
BLO690	92	Scammell 6wl flat lorry	4.1939	New in 1.1935 to Fisher Renwick; acquired by Pearce Haulage Co for the London night trunk service; 1949 to British Road Services
BXV560	93	Scammell 6wl flat lorry	4.1939	New in 6.1935 to Fisher Renwick; acquired by Pearce Haulage Co. for the London night trunk service; 1949 to British Road Services
BLL248	94	Scammell 6wl flat lorry	4.1939	New in 11.1934 to Fisher Renwick; acquired for the London night trunk service; 1951 to British Road Services
BLL835	95	Scammell 6wl flat lorry	4.1939	New in 12.1934 to Fisher Renwick; acquired for the London night trunk service; 1951 to British Road Services
BLN963	96	Scammell 6wl flat lorry	4.1939	New in 1.1935 to Fisher Renwick; acquired for the London night trunk service; 1951 to British Road Services
CDW847		Fordson 2ton lorry	4.1940	Supplied by Tydesley, Welshpool
CDW905		Dodge lorry	10.1940	Supplied by Normans, Cardiff; 1951 to British Road Services
CDW909	101	ERF articulated tractor unit	1.1941	Supplied ex-works under MOT licence
CDW910	102	ERF articulated tractor unit	2.1941	Supplied ex-works under MOT licence
CDW912	63	Caterpillar tractor	3.1941	Tracked vehicle for timber extraction
CDW917	103	ERF articulated tractor unit	5.1941	Supplied ex-works under MOT licence
CDW919	104	Foden timber tractor	5.1941	Supplied under MOT licence
CDW935	105	Scammell articulated tractor unit	9.1941	Supplied under MOT licence
CDW944	106	Scammell articulated tractor unit	9.1941	Supplied under MOT licence
CDW951		Bedford 5ton dropside lorry	10.1941	Supplied under MOT Licence; 1951 to British Road Services
CDW952		Bedford 5ton dropside lorry	10.1941	Supplied under MOT licence; 1951 to British Road Services

A large boxed load being carried for the Bristol Aeroplane Co. Ltd. in 1938 on a petrol-engined Bedford low-loader DW9726 (27). This vehicle had been supplied new in January, 1936 by Atlas Garages, Newport.

(Below) Acquired for the London nightly trunk service, this Scammell 8-wheel flat lorry ADW617 (81) was eventually converted to a tanker.

(Above) This Dodge tipper, index no: ADW401 was supplied to WYNNS in December, 1936 by Morse Motors, Cardiff. The firm operated a large fleet of tippers particularly in and around the Cardiff area.

Excavated materials being loaded onto Bedford tipper BDW957 (88) which joined the WYNNS fleet in October, 1938.

This Scammell 45ton tractor unit CDW33 (87) fitted with solid rear tyres joined the fleet in 1938.
This vehicle was an important unit of the wartime heavy haulage fleet.

Seen operating as part of the WYNNS tanker fleet are Scammell LDW227 (227) of 1955 and ERF CDW910 (102)
of 1941, With fourteen years between them it clearly shows that the firm made them last.

Foden 6wl drawbar tractor DDW18 (112) acquired in 1942 is seen drawing a four axle trailer with a 120ton hammer block. This 60ton vehicle was the mainstay of the WYNNS heavy haulage fleet during and immediately after the Second World War.

This Scammell articulated lorry, index no: DDW226 (132) was acquired in 1946.

Two views of the Foden drawbar tractor, index number DDW18:
(Above): Carrying a transformer weighing 103 tons on a solid tyred trailer, and
(Below): carrying a 90 ton transformer in slung position - thus reducing the travelling height.

Index No.	Fleet No.	Vehicle.	Date Aqd.	Notes.
CDW974		Bedford 5ton dropside lorry	1.1942	Supplied under MOT licence by Atlas Garages, Newport; 1951 to British Road Services
CDW975		Bedford 5ton dropside lorry	1.1942	Supplied under MOT licence by Atlas Garages, Newport; 1951 to British Road Services
CDW980	109	Foden timber tractor	1.1942	Supplied under MOT Licence
CDW987		John Deere agricultural tractor	2.1942	Still using many horses this tractor was used on WYNNS land
DDW18	112	Foden DG 6wl 60ton drawbar tractor	7.1942	Supplied under MOT licence; 1958 broken up
DDW20		Fordson tractor	8.1942	
DDW21	58	Bedford OXC/Scammell articulated lorry	8.1942	Supplied under MOT licence by Atlas Garages, Newport
DDW22	68	Bedford OXC/Scammell articulated lorry	9.1942	Supplied under MOT licence by Atlas Garages, Newport
DDW27	78	Bedford OXC/Scammell articulated lorry	10.1942	Supplied under MOT licence
DDW30		Bedford OXC/Scammell articulated lorry	12.1942	Supplied under MOT licence to Pearce Haulage Co.; 1949 to British Road Services
UC33—		Scammell timber tractor	c1942	Origins unknown, possibly a rebuild; only part index number known
UC5838		Scammell timber tractor	1942	Originally a Pickfords vehicle date unknown; subsequently rebuilt as a demonstrator timber tractor by Scammell from whom WYNNS bought it.
DDW35		Scammell articulated tractor unit	2.1943	Supplied under MOT licence
DDW49		Scammell articulated tractor unit	7.1943	Supplied under MOT licence
DDW52		Ford tractor	6.1943	
LME89	115	Unipower Hannibal timber tractor	1944	Demonstration vehicle supplied under MOT licence
DDW76	116	Bedford tipper	6.1944	Supplied under MOT licence
DDW77	117	Bedford tipper	7.1944	Supplied under MOT licence
DDW78	118	Bedford tipper	7.1944	Supplied under MOT licence
DDW85	120	Scammell articulated tractor unit	8.1944	Supplied under MOT licence
DDW88	121	Ford tractor	8.1944	

Index No.	Fleet No.	Vehicle.	Date Aqd.	Notes.
DDW92	122	Scammell articulated tractor unit	10.1944	Supplied under MOT licence
DDW100	123	Dodge dropside lorry	1.1945	Supplied under MOT licence; 1951 to British Road Services
DDW109	124	Bedford/Scammell articulated lorry	5.1945	Supplied under MOT licence
DDW141	125	Bedford/Scammell articulated lorry	6.1945	Supplied under MOT licence
DDW142	126	Scammell articulated tractor unit	9.1945	
DDW144		Morris mobile crane	4.1945	I doubt that this vehicle existed as the number was subsequently re-registered as a Fordson 10cwt van for other owners
DDW160	127	Scammell articulated tractor unit	6.1945	
DDW161	128	Scammell articulated tractor unit	6.1945	
DDW165	129	Scammell articulated tractor unit	9.1945	
DDW173	130	Bedford 5ton dropside lorry	12.1945	
DDW174	131	Bedford 5ton dropside lorry	12.1945	
DDW226	132	Scammell articulated tractor unit	2.1946	
DDW287	134	Bedford 5ton dropside lorry	4.1946	
DDW340	133	AEC Monarch 7.5ton dropside lorry	6.1946	
DDW495	140	Scammell Pioneer drawbar tractor	1.1946	ex-WD; rebuilt by WYNNS from a tank transporter
DDW496		Scammell tractor	8.1946	ex-WD
DDW502		Scammell articulated tractor unit	7.1946	
DDW601	137	FWD timber tractor	9.1946	ex-WD
DDW605		FWD timber tractor	9.1946	ex-WD
DDW606	142	Commer 2ton lorry	9.1946	
DDW678		Commer 2ton lorry	12.1946	
DDW771		FWD timber tractor	12.1946	ex-WD
DDW777		Guy 5ton tipper	12.1946	ex-WD
DDW806		Vauxhall 14hp motor car	11.1946	
DDW889	144	FWD timber tractor	1.1947	ex-WD
DDW890	145	FWD timber tractor	2.1947	ex-WD
DDW891	146	FWD timber tractor	6.1947	ex-WD

Index No.	Fleet No.	Vehicle.	Date Aqd.	Notes.
DDW988		General haulage tractor	3.1947	Make & details unknown
HPP814		Scammell Pioneer drawbar tractor	c1947	ex-WD
EDW5	147	Chevrolet 4/5ton timber tractor	3.1947	ex-WD
EDW6	150	Fordson tractor	3.1947	
EDW92	158	Douglas timber tractor	5.1947	ex-WD; actually registered as an AEC
EDW93	149	Chevrolet timber tractor	8.1947	ex-WD
EDW94	148	Chevrolet timber tractor	8.1947	ex-WD
EDW95	160	Diamond T 980 drawbar tractor	5.1947	ex-WD; preserved by Howard Francis, Ewyas Harold, Pontrilas, Herefordshire
EDW96	161	Diamond T 980 drawbar tractor	8.1947	ex-WD
EDW97		FWD timber tractor	5.1947	ex-WD
HHW755	151	Austin timber lorry	1947	Dated from 1943; bought from the Forestry Commission
HHW756	152	Austin timber lorry	1947	Dated from 1943; bought from the Forestry Commission
HHY949	155	Caterpillar tractor	1947	Dated from 1943; bought from the Forestry Commission; tracked vehicle used for timber extraction
JAE95	156	Unipower timber tractor	1947	Dated from 1944; bought from the Forestry Commission
EDW158	200	Ward LaFrance wrecker	5.1947	ex-WD
EDW240		Commer 2ton lorry	7.1947	
EDW241		FWD timber tractor	7.1947	ex-WD
EDW242	201	Federal 6WD twin-boom wrecker	7.1947	ex-WD
EDW339	164	Bedford/Scammell articulated lorry	8.1947	
EDW340	202	Ward LaFrance wrecker	8.1947	ex-WD
EDW404		Ford motor car	9.1947	
EDW481	166	FWD timber tractor	11.1947	ex-WD
EDW482		Ford tractor	11.1947	
EDW574	167	Dodge 5ton tipper	4.1948	
EDW575		Bedford/Scammell articulated lorry	2.1948	
EDW597		Crossley 4WD tackle wagon	4.1948	

Index No.	Fleet No.	Vehicle.	Date Aqd.	Notes.
EDW599	203	Ward LaFrance wrecker	4.1948	ex-WD
DF6042		Sentinel 6wl steam tipper	1948	ex-Powell Duffryn; bought from National Coal Board
WO7705		Sentinel 6wl steam tipper	1948	ex-Powell Duffryn; bought from National Coal Board
TN5846		Sentinel 6wl steam tipper	1948	ex-Powell Duffryn; bought from National Coal Board
ANY135	175	Sentinel 4wl steam tar carrier	1948	Dated from 5.1935, ex-Powell Duffryn; bought from National Coal Board; Operated until 12.1952
EDW601	176	Foden 6wl flat lorry	4.1948	ex-WD
EDW602	177	Foden 6wl flat lorry	9.1948	ex-WD
EDW603	204	Morris mobile crane	2.1948	Date unknown; bought from Mole & Company, Newport; 1982 transferred to Wynns Heavy Haulage, Stafford
EDW625		Vauxhall motor car	3.1948	
EDW710		Karrier tackle wagon	4.1948	ex-WD
EDW727		Ferguson agricultural tractor	4.1948	
EDW767		Willys Jeep	6.1948	ex-WD
EDW809	82	Caterpillar tractor	5.1948	Tracked vehicle used for timber extraction
EDW810	83	Caterpillar tractor	6.1948	Tracked vehicle used for timber extraction
EDW868	165	Diamond T 980 drawbar tractor	7.1948	ex-WD
EDW998	84	Caterpillar tractor	10.1948	Tracked vehicle used for timber extraction
FDW4		Ward LaFrance wrecker	10.1948	ex-WD
FDW60	65	Foden 6wl flat lorry	11.1948	ex-WD; owned by Pearce Haulage Co.; 1949 to British Road Services
FDW61	66	Foden 6wl flat lorry	11.1948	ex-WD; Owned by Pearce Haulage Co.; 1949 to British Road Services
FDW77	77	FWD timber tractor	10.1948	ex-WD
FDW79	79	FWD timber tractor	5.1950	ex-WD

This Scammell Pioneer drawbar tractor, DDW495 (140) acquired in 1946, was converted from an Army tank transporter. Driver Jake Healey is pictured infront of his vehicle.

Another Scammell Pioneer owned by WYNNS is this vehicle HPP814 seen hauling a boiler.

(Left): Two views of FWD SU-COE timber tractor DDW601 (137) engaged on round timber extraction. A total of twelve of these useful ex-WD vehicles were acquired by WYNNS, this being the first. In addition the firm also employed Chevolet, AEC, Thornycroft, Douglas and Unipower timber tractors.

Timber extraction formed a big part of the firm's business, and as well as a depot at Welshpool in Mid-Wales devoted to this activity, vehicles were stationed at various locations throughout Wales where long term work was being undertaken. At some locations living vans, similar to those towed by steamrollers, were provided for the crews who were unable to return home at the end of the days work. With the transfer of WYNNS into the United Transport Group this business was disposed of, partly due to the contraction in the volume of timber being felled, and because it was not a core activity of the group.

(Above) A caterpillar tractor, dragging felled timber.

Post-war Britain saw considerable industrial expansion and although WYNNS had operated the Foden DG 6-wheel - 60ton drawbar tractor from 1942 they needed to expand their heavy haulage fleet to take full benefit of the work now available. H.P. (Percy) Wynn was impressed with the capabilities of the United States manufactured Diamond T tank transporter drawbar tractor which soon became available for civilian use. This vehicle type was to form the basis of the fleet, together with six heavier Pacific units, for some twenty years. Although the twenty-two operated Diamond T tractors are listed in the main fleet list, for interest I list them here together.

Index No.	Fleet No.	Date Entered Service.	Index No.	Fleet No.	Date Entered Service.
EDW95	160	5.1947	NDW232	247	12.1956
EDW96	161	8.1947	NDW925	248	6.1957
EDW868	165	7.1948	ODW937	262	6.1958
FDW533	-	6.1949	PDW321	266	6.1958
FDW922	186	4.1950	PDW927	276	3.1959
GDW313	187	9.1950	RDW976	281	5.1959
GDW800	-	6.1951	TDW241	279	11.1959
HDW107	199	12.1951	1300DW	90	10.1962
HDW572	212	8.1952	3630DW	91	10.1963
KDW560	184	3.1954	BDW277B	249	12.1964
LDW810	234	9.1955	EDW782D	50	3.1966

Originally fitted with the Hercules petrol engine, WYNNS were quick to fit the vehicles with a Cummins diesel engine. As some of the Diamond Ts were rebuilt in WYNNS own workshops they were fitted with new cabs, first the Nash Morgan type and later the in-house Anderson type. The second vehicle to enter the fleet - EDW96 even had a chrome surround fitted to the windscreen glass. HDW107 was subsequently converted into an articulated tractor unit, but as a drawbar was used on one occasion in conjunction with Atlantic Container Line in unloading and loading one of their RO/RO ships at Nova Scotia and New York. Around 1960 PDW321 was fitted out as a wrecker. Happily some of these WYNNS vehicles have found their way into private hands and preservation. My own recollections of the Diamond T are of a no frills, cold in Winter/hot in Summer cramped cab which always had a strong smell of diesel fuel. It was nonetheless an extremely useful tool which was eventually superseded by the Scammell Contractor range, but had given over twenty years of valuable service to the firm.

(Overleaf): Diamond T - EDW95 (160) with the assistance of a Scammell 4-wheel ballast tractor, haul a Lima excavator through Worcester. Note that by this time, 1960, the Diamond T has been recabbed with a Nash Morgan manufactured type.

(Top Left) A pair of Bedford 5ton dropside lorries, DDW174 (131) and DDW287 (134) loading at the premises of Pan Products, Dock Street, Newport.

(Bottom Left) The second Diamond T EDW96 (161) is shown double-heading Pacific GDW585 (196) as they climb Barrack Hill, Newport with a transformer. Two more Diamond Ts bring up the rear. (South Wales Argus).

DANGER
WIDE
LOAD

EDW 95

WYNNS

An imposing view of two Diamond Ts hauling an excavator. The vehicles are seen travelling down Stow Hill, Newport, from the direction of St Woolas Cathedral towards the Westgate Square. The leading tractor is EDW96 (161) which entered service in August, 1947. Note the chrome trim around the windscreen glass.

Index No.	Fleet No.	Vehicle.	Date Aqd.	Notes.
FDW80	80	FWD timber tractor	2.1949	ex-WD
FDW181	181	Foden 6wl flat lorry	1.1949	ex-WD; 1951 to British Road Services
FDW182	182	Foden 6wl flat lorry	1.1949	ex-WD; 1951 to British Road Services
FDW183	183	Foden 6wl flat lorry	5.1949	ex-WD; 1951 to British Road Services
FDW184	184	Foden 6wl flat lorry	8.1949	ex-WD; 1951 to British Road Services
FDW216	205	Ward LaFrance wrecker	1.1949	ex-WD
FDW333		Humber Super Snipe motor car	3.1949	Owned by S. Wynn
FDW339	38	Bedford/Scammell articulated lorry	7.1949	
FDW385	44	Chevrolet 5ton timber tractor	4.1949	ex-WD
FDW386	45	Chevrolet 5ton timber tractor	5.1949	ex-WD
FDW466		Ford Pilot 30hp motor car	5.1949	Owned by H.P. Wynn
FDW500		Morris motor car	5.1949	Owned by S. Wynn
FDW533		Diamond T 980 drawbar tractor	6.1949	ex-WD
FDW635	15	Fordson industrial tractor	8.1949	
FDW686		Vauxhall motor car	9.1949	Owned by G.P. Wynn
JC7958	20	Dodge 4WD van	3.1949	New to United States Navy; later to a farmer in Caernarvon; 1949 to WYNNS; 8.1959 to Price, Bridge Street Garage, Newport; 12.1961 scrapped
TV9649	23	Leyland Cub tractor	1949	Dated from 1935, bought secondhand
EVJ805	24	Chevrolet timber tractor	1949	ex-WD; bought secondhand
GLD588	25	Bedford articulated tractor unit	1949	Dated from 1942; bought secondhand
FDW750	113	Bedford 3ton tipper	10.1949	
FDW751	114	Bedford 3ton tipper	11.1949	
FDW752	207	Thornycroft-Coles mobile crane	1.1950	ex-WD
FDW792	188	Bedford dropside lorry	5.1950	
FDW910	189	Unipower Forrester timber tractor	2.1950	
FDW911	190	Unipower Forrester timber tractor	2.1950	
FDW912	191	Unipower Forrester timber tractor	2.1950	
FDW916	122	Bedford 3ton tipper	1.1950	

Index No.	Fleet No.	Vehicle.	Date Aqd.	Notes.
FDW922	186	Diamond T 981 drawbar tractor	4.1950	ex-WD
FDW945		Ford motor car	2.1950	
FDW992	99	Caterpillar tractor	3.1950	Tracked vehicle used for timber extraction
GDW17	97	Caterpillar tractor	3.1950	Tracked vehicle used for timber extraction
GDW18	127	Fordson Thames 8ton articulated tractor unit	11.1950	
GDW192		Chevrolet 4ton lorry	8.1950	ex-WD
GDW203		Ford motor car	8.1950	
GDW277	192	Pacific drawbar tractor	9.1950	ex-WD; 1969 rebuilt and re-registered as NDW345G. Named - Dreadnought
GDW313	187	Diamond T 980 drawbar tractor	9.1950	ex-WD
JLR985	208	Rapier yard crane	1950	Originally owned by the Great Western Railway, later British Railways
GDW381		Ford motor car	10.1950	Owned by S. Wynn
GDW585	196	Pacific drawbar tractor	5.1951	ex-WD; 1970 used to carry out a contract in Cyprus and sold to the customer, re-registered locally as FDO13. Named - Helpmate
GDW800		Diamond T 980 drawbar tractor	6.1951	ex-WD
HDW43	210	Scammell articulated tractor unit	10.1951	
HDW88	211	Scammell articulated tractor unit	12.1951	
HDW107	199	Diamond T drawbar tractor	12.1951	ex-WD; later operated as an articulated tractor unit.
HDW122	193	Pacific drawbar tractor	12.1951	ex-WD; this was the leading vehicle involved in the Hixon Railway Disaster on 6.1.1968; Named Challenger
HDW249		Karrier 4WD tackle wagon	3.1952	ex-WD
HDW519	213	Scammell articulated tractor unit	7.1952	
HDW562		Diamond T drawbar tractor	1952	Application made in error see next entry
HDW572	212	Diamond T 980 drawbar tractor	8.1952	ex-WD
HDW623		Ford Prefect motor car	9.1952	
HDW710		Ford Zephyr motor car	10.1952	

Index No.	Fleet No.	Vehicle.	Date Aqd.	Notes.
HDW797		Morris Minor motor car	12.1952	
HDW898	43	Fordson agricultural tractor	2.1953	
HDW928	98	Caterpillar tractor	3.1953	Tracked vehicle used for timber extraction
PDE53	33	Caterpillar tractor	1953	Tracked vehicle used for timber extraction; bought second hand
HDW996	214	Scammell articulated tractor unit	4.1953	
JDW33		Ford Consul motor car	5.1953	Owned by Miss Wynn
JDW48		Thornycroft Mighty Antar drawbar Tractor	5.1953	Built for the Snowy Mountain Hydro-Electric Scheme in Australia, together with a Crane 100ft. trailer; licensed and tested by WYNNS prior to export.
JDW49		Thornycroft Mighty Antar drawbar Tractor	5.1953	as above.
EDW640	26	Austin van	1953	Bought from F. Hammond, Newport; dated from 10.1949
KG5004		AEC Regent omnibus	1953	No details other than believed owned by Robert Wynn & Sons (Manchester) Ltd
HDW468	220	Scammell articulated tractor unit	1953	New to British Road Services, Newport in 7.1952
HDW469	221	Scammell articulated tractor unit	1953	New to British Road Services, Newport, in 7.1952
JDW395	215	Bedford 5ton tipper	10.1953	
JDW621	216	Karrier 4WD tackle wagon	11.1953	
JDW712	217	Bedford 5ton tipper	12.1953	
GXV224	218	Bedford articulated tractor unit	1953	Dated from 1942; bought secondhand
	10	Clarkter yard tug	1953	No other details
	108	Mercury yard tug	c1953	Preserved by Joseph Willson, Pontypool
	100	Dodge lorry	1953	No other details
JDW800		Morris Minor motor car	2.1954	
KDW275	219	Scammell 4wl drawbar tractor	9.1954	
KDW455	222	Scammell articulated tractor unit	12.1954	
KDW560	184	Diamond T 980 drawbar tractor	3.1954	ex-WD

Index No.	Fleet No.	Vehicle.	Date Aqd.	Notes.
CBK856	222	Foden drawbar tractor	1954	New in 1940 to Messrs Parks, Portsmouth, thence Pickfords
LUW348	223	AEC Monarch 7.5ton flat lorry	1954	New in 1950 to Arlington Motors, thence Pickfords
GKC549	225	Scammell 4wl drawbar tractor	1954	New in 1940 to Edward Box, Liverpool, thence Pickfords.
GKC866	224	Scammell 4wl drawbar tractor	1954	New in 1940 to Edward Box, Liverpool, thence Pickfords
JD9082	228	Scammell 4wl drawbar tractor	1954	New in 1939 to E.W. Rudd, Stratford, thence Pickfords
DUS2	229	Scammell 4wl drawbar tractor	1954	New in 1943 to Road Engines & Kerr, Glasgow, thence Pickfords
RJ5022	230	Leyland Cub articulated tractor unit	1954	Dated from 1935 - origins unknown; bought from Pickfords
TJ4299	231	Leyland Cub articulated tractor unit	1954	Dated from 1935 -origins unknown; bought from Pickfords
KDW894		Jaguar motor car	2.1955	Number transferred from RTV990
LDW73	233	Bedford articulated tractor unit	4.1955	
LDW227	227	Scammell articulated tractor unit	5.1955	
LDW810	234	Diamond T 980 drawbar tractor	9.1955	ex-WD
LDW835	235	Bedford articulated tractor unit	10.1955	
LKG877	236	Ford van	1955	Dated from 1954, bought second hand
MDW69		Vauxhall Cresta motor car	11.1955	
MDW94		Morris Minor motor car	12.1955	
MDW100		Ford Prefect motor car	11.1955	
MDW298	237	Bedford articulated tractor unit	5.1956	
MDW880	241	Thornycroft tackle wagon	6.1956	ex-WD
MDW947	244	Scammell Mountaineer drawbar Tractor	8.1956	Owned by Robert Wynn & Sons (Manchester) Ltd
MDW951	245	Scammell articulated tractor unit	12.1956	Subsequently converted to a drawbar tractor, later sold to British Nuclear Fuels for internal use; now preserved by Glyn Salathial, Nantyglo

WYNN'S PRESERVATION
GROUP

EDW 95

WYNNS
RECOVERY
VEHICLE

PDW 321

(Left) Shown negotiating Chain Bridge, between Usk and Abergavenny, are the preserved Diamond Ts: EDW95 (160) and ODW937 (262) .

(Bottom Left) Seen with dark blue body and red chassis, wheels and bonnet - preserved Diamond T - EDW95 is shown at a show while owned by Viscount Presswood. Fitted with a tarpauline cover to the ballast box, he had bought the vehicle from Cricklewood Garage, near London. It is thought by this time the vehicle had received some attention involving parts from a number of other units. It was from this source that Howard Francis of Ewyas Harold, bought the vehicle for restoration, and often uses it to raise money for charity.

(Bottom Centre & Bottom Right) Registered in 1958 Diamond T - PDW321 (266) only had a short career in heavy haulage before conversion to a wrecker.

Although purchasing large numbers of the Diamond T drawbar tractor, WYNNS were interested in acquiring a number of larger vehicles, and to this end the U.S. built Pacific M26 drawbar tractor fitted the bill. Unlike the Diamond T these vehicles required considerable attention before entering service and were totally rebuilt in-house. In all six of the type were used as follows:

Index No.	Fleet No.	Name.	Date Entered Service.	
GDW277	192	Dreadnought	9.1950	Later rebuilt with Scammell parts, and re-registered in 1969 as NDW345G.
GDW585	196	Helpmate	5.1951	Carried out a contract in Cyprus in 1970, sold locally at conclusion.
HDW122	193	Conqueror	12.1951	Leading tractor at the Hixon Railway Disaster on 6.1.1968
YDW356	195	Challenger	9.1961	
1570DW	194	Valiant	12.1962	
ADW228B	197	Enterprise	7.1964	Preserved and recently rebuilt by Mike Lawrence of Somerset

(Below): Pacific drawbar tractor with a 105 ton locomotive arriving at The Festival of Britain site in London, in 1951. The contract involved hauling the locomotive, which was an exhibit, from the Surrey Commercial Dock, on its arrival from Glasgow by sea.

(opposite): Two views of Pacific GDW277, (above): Hauling a transformer.
(below): transporting a crane girder at the Old Green Crossing, Newport.
(overleaf): The 1951 registered Pacific drawbar tractor GDW277 (192) 'Dreadnought'.

STAFFORD
WYNNS
NEWPORT CARDIFF LONDON
DREADNOUGHT
192
192
GDW-277

Index No.	Fleet No.	Vehicle.	Date Aqd.	Notes.
	243	Bedford petrol bowser	1956	ex-WD; used as a static fuel tank at Shaftesbury Street yard and later at Albany Street yard
NDW44	242	Thornycroft tackle wagon	8.1956	ex-WD
NDW232	247	Diamond T 981 drawbar tractor	12.1956	ex-WD
NDW233	240	Thornycroft tackle wagon	11.1956	ex-WD
NDW460	250	Ford Escort estate car	2.1957	Owned by Robert Wynn & Sons (Manchester) Ltd
NDW500		Ford Prefect motor car	2.1957	
NDW548	249	Thornycroft tackle wagon	3.1957	ex-WD
NDW600		Jaguar motor car	3.1957	Number transferred from KDW894
NDW743	209	Thornycroft Coles mobile crane	4.1957	ex-WD
NDW808		Ford Zephyr motor car	5.1957	
NDW925	248	Diamond T 980 drawbar tractor	6.1957	ex-WD
NOA636	246	Ford Thames tipper	1957	Dated from 1953, bought secondhand
ODW95	251	Thornycroft tackle wagon	10.1957	ex-WD; Owned by Wynns (Engineering) Ltd
JD9083	239	Scammell 4wl drawbar tractor	1957	New in 1939 to E.W. Rudd, Stratford, thence Pickfords
NAX151	252	Commer tipper	1957	New in 11.1954 to J. Murphy, Ynysddu
JRU902	253	Austin van	1957	Dated from 1950, bought secondhand
ODW457	259	Commer articulated tractor unit	1957	
ODW410		Commer van	10.1957	Owned by G. Wynn
ODW464		Humber Hawk motor car	11.1957	
ODW478	257	Scammell Mountaineer drawbar tractor	12.1957	
ODW479	259?	Commer articulated tractor unit	11.1957	
ODW480	260	Bedford articulated tractor unit	12.1957	
GGU262	255	Scammell articulated tractor unit	1957	New in 1941 to the Petrol Pool, thence Shell Mex
GXC463	256	Scammell articulated tractor unit	1957	New in 1941 to the Petrol Pool, thence Shell Mex
767ENK		Scammell Super Constructor drawbar tractor	1958	Demonstrator vehicle on test from Scammell

Index No.	Fleet No.	Vehicle.	Date Aqd.	Notes.
ODW620	263	Coles mobile crane	1.1958	
ODW680	264	Scammell 4wl drawbar tractor	9.1958	
NDH337	261	Ford Thames articulated tractor unit	1957	
ODW888		Rover motor car	5.1958	
ODW937	262	Diamond T 981 drawbar tractor	6.1958	ex-WD; preserved by Steve Roberts, Cwmbran
PDW42	258	AEC Matador timber tractor	5.1958	ex-WD
PDW319	265	Thornycroft tackle wagon	1958	ex-WD
PDW321	266	Diamond T 980 drawbar tractor	6.1958	ex-WD; Owned by Robert Wynn & Sons (Manchester) Ltd; 1960 converted to a wrecker; preserved.
PDW412	267	Guy Warrior articulated tractor unit	8.1958	
PDW504	268	Lorain mobile crane	8.1958	Owned by Wynns (Engineering) Ltd
PDW600	269	Guy Warrior articulated tractor unit	1.1959	
PDW848	254	Thornycroft tackle wagon	12.1958	ex-WD; owned by Wynns (Engineering) Ltd
PDW849	274	Guy Otter tipper	11.1958	
PDW850	275	Guy Otter tipper	11.1958	
PDW927	276	Diamond T 980 drawbar tractor	3.1959	ex-WD
KKG865	270	Thornycroft flat lorry	1959	New in 1955 to Edward England Ltd., Fruit & Vegetable Merchants, Cardiff
HYK659	271	Ransomes Rapier yard crane	1959	New in 1948 to British Waterways Board; subsequently sold to Logan, Goytre
RDW65		AEC Matador timber tractor	1.1959	ex-WD
RDW259		Ford Anglia motor car	2.1959	Owned by Robert Wynn & Sons (Manchester) Ltd
RDW530	272	Coles mobile crane	4.1959	Owned by Crindau Garages Ltd
RDW531	273	Morris mobile crane	4.1959	Owned by Wynns (Engineering) Ltd
RDW610		Ford Consul motor car	4.1959	
RDW876		Jaguar motor car	7.1959	Number transferred from NDW600
RDW976	281	Diamond T 980 drawbar tractor	5.1959	ex-WD
DFK734	277	Foden articulated tractor unit	1959	New in 1949 to Weaver, Worcester, thence British Road Services and Pickfords

Index No.	Fleet No.	Vehicle.	Date Aqd.	Notes.
GXX15	278	Pacific drawbar tractor	1959	ex-WD; believed used as spares or as a donor vehicle
LEA475	280	Scammell articulated tractor unit	1959	Dated from 1955, bought secondhand
XJW602	283	Guy Formidable 8wl tanker	1959	Guy demonstrator new in 1959
SDW200		Ford Zodiac motor car	6.1959	
SDW817	284	Guy Invincible articulated tractor unit	9.1959	
TDW231	285	Guy Warrior articulated tractor unit	11.1959	
TDW232	286	Guy Warrior articulated tractor unit	10.1959	
TDW241	279	Diamond T 980 drawbar tractor	11.1959	ex-WD
TDW287	287	Guy Invincible articulated tractor unit	12.1959	
TDW288	288	Guy Invincible articulated tractor unit	1.1960	
TDW289	289	Guy Invincible articulated tractor unit	1.1960	
TDW309	2	Bedford 15cwt van	11.1959	Owned by Robert Wynn & Sons (Manchester) Ltd
TDW310	3	Bedford 15cwt van	12.1959	Owned by Crindau Garages Ltd
TDW606		Ford Popular motor car	12.1959	
TDW835	290	Guy Invincible articulated tractor unit	2.1960	
TDW836	292	Guy Invincible articulated tractor unit	3.1960	
296ATG	291	Guy Warrior tipper	1960	New in 1960, bought secondhand
TDW900		Ford Zodiac motor car	1.1960	
TDW990	293	Guy Invincible 8wl flat lorry	3.1960	Records show as being owned by Robert Wynn & Sons (Birmingham) Ltd - no other vehicle is thus shown, therefore may be a mistake; however the vehicle certainly existed
TDW991	294	Guy Invincible 8wl flat lorry	3.1960	
TDW992	295	Guy Invincible tipper	2.1960	
TDW993	296	Guy Invincible tipper	2.1960	
UDW140		Ford Escort motor car	3.1960	
UDW200		Ford Popular motor car	3.1960	

Index No.	Fleet No.	Vehicle.	Date Aqd.	Notes.
UDW222		Ford Popular motor car	3.1960	
UDW690	297	Guy Warrior articulated tractor unit	4.1960	
UDW691	298	Guy Warrior articulated tractor unit	4.1960	
UDW692	299	Ford 12 seater minibus	4.1960	
UDW875	153	Guy Warrior 8wl tanker	5.1960	Converted to a flat in 1965
VDW248	201	Thornycroft Coles mobile crane	6.1960	ex-WD; owned by Wynns (Engineering) Ltd
VDW324	180	Scammell Highwayman articulated tractor unit	9.1960	
VDW325	181	Scammell Highwayman articulated tractor unit	7.1960	Owned by Robert Wynn & Sons (Manchester) Ltd
VDW576		Rover 105 motor car	7.1960	Number transferred from ODW888
VDW704		Ford Consul motor car	9.1960	Owned by S. Wynn
XWO21	182	Bedford pickup	1960	New in 1960. Bought from Raymond International, Llanwern Steelworks
PNV826	183	Bedford pickup	1960	New in 1957, bought from Raymond International, Llanwern Steelworks
PDW339	151	Bedford van	1960	New in 1958 to F. Hammond, Newport
UBO729	154	Ford Thames Trader tipper	1960	New in 1959, bought secondhand
TAX352	119	Scammell articulated tractor unit	1960	New in 1958 to E.B. Rees, Usk; subsequently passed to Logan, Goytre and converted to a wrecker; survives in that ownership
HGK543	156	Scammell articulated tractor unit	1960	New in 1946 to General Roadways, thence British Road Services, and to E.B. Rees, Usk; do not believe that WYNNS used this vehicle as sold later in 1960
508HRF	162	Leyland Octopus 8wl flat lorry	1960	New in 1956; bought from E.B. Rees, Usk; no other details
		BMC tipper	c1960	No details, origins unknown
OCT393	157	BMC flat lorry	1960	Origins unknown, bought secondhand
395TMC	163	Ford Thames Trader tipper	1960	New in 1959, bought secondhand
YLD596	190	Ford Thames Trader tipper	1960	Bought secondhand
YNM627	191	Ford Thames Trader tipper	1960	Bought secondhand
DEP426	4	Standard Vanguard pickup	1960	Dated from 1953, bought secondhand

Originally entering the fleet as an articulated tractor unit Scammell MDW951 (245) dating from 1956. The vehicle was subsequently converted to a drawbar tractor (above) and eventually sold to British Nuclear Fuels for internal use. It is now preserved by Glyn Salathial, Nantyglo, and (below) seen in Abergavenny Cattle Market, prior to joining the Abergavenny Steam Rally.

(Above): This Scammell articulated tractor unit, index number: HDW468 (220) bought in 1953 was new to British Road Services, Newport, the previous year.

(Below & Overleaf): The 1959 registered Diamond T - RDW976 (281) negotiates an overbridge with a stated clearance of 13ft 6ins, with its crawler crane load.

HIGGS AND HILL
LIMITED
LONDON
LEEDS COVENTRY
38 RB
Heinz
WYNNS

Above: Over the pits in the workshops are Ford Thames Trader tipper XWO218 (71) bought from the Star Brick & Tile Co. Ltd., Ponthir in 1961, Guy Warrior 8-wheel tanker YDW115 (156) and Lorain mobile crane PDW504 (268).

Top Left: During the construction of Llanwern Steelworks in the three years from 1959 large quantities of material was transported from Newport Docks to the new site. In this view four vehicles wait to load ex-ship: Guy TDW836 (292), Guy XDW300 (152), Scammell DDW226 (132) and Guy TDW835 (290).

Left: Considerable quantities of steel tubes manufactured by Stewart & Lloyd, Corporation Road, Newport, were transported. This photograph shows seven loads about to leave the factory headed by Guy Invincible 611DW (95). This work increased during the conversion to North Sea gas during the early 1970s.

Index No.	Fleet No.	Vehicle.	Date Aqd.	Notes.
GEP438	7	Standard Vanguard pickup	1960	Dated from 1956, bought secondhand
HWB747	5	Landrover	1960	Dated from 1954, bought secondhand; may have carried index number DW31
WDW63	159	Guy Invincible 8wl tanker	1960	
WDW100	100	Guy Invincible 6wl drawbar tractor	11.1960	More commonly used as an articulated tractor unit
MUD527	6	Bedford pickup	1961	Dated from 1958, bought secondhand
448AFC	8	Willys Jeep	1961	ex-WD; bought secondhand
JUU667	11	Ransomes Rapier yard crane	1961	New in 1948 to British Railways
WDW319		Thornycroft tackle wagon	11.1960	ex-WD; owned by Wynns (Engineering) Ltd
WDW381	170	Guy Warrior 8wl tanker	1961	
WDW382	167	Guy Warrior 8wl tanker	1.1961	
WDW383	169	Scammell Highwayman articulated tractor unit	1.1961	
WDW485		Ford Zephyr motor car	12.1960	
WDW670		Ford Zephyr motor car	2.1961	
WDW671		Ford Consul motor car	2.1961	
WDW672		Ford Prefect motor car	2.1961	Owned by Crindau Garages Ltd
WDW734		Rover 3 litre motor car	3.1961	Number transferred from ODW888
WDW881		Guy Warrior articulated tractor unit	4.1961	
WDW882	187	Lorain mobile crane	3.1961	Owned by Wynns (Engineering) Ltd
BJV536	172	AEC Matador breakdown lorry	1961	ex-WD; bought secondhand; owned by Crindau Garages Ltd
XTG58	171	Foden 8wl tanker	1961	New in 1958 to Beales, Cefn Cribwr, Glam.
MNA1	173	Bedford articulated tractor unit	1961	Dated from 1951, bought secondhand
MBX967	174	Bedford flat lorry	1961	Dated from 1956, bought secondhand
XDW300	152	Guy Invincible 8wl flat lorry	4.1961	
XDW750		Austin A55 motor car	6.1961	
YDW22	216	AEC Matador tackle wagon	8.1961	ex-WD; Owned by Wynns (Engineering) Ltd.; Was fitted with a Bedford cab without badging
YDW115	156	Guy Warrior 8wl tanker	8.1961	
YDW340	142	Guy Warrior articulated tractor unit	10.1961	

Index No.	Fleet No.	Vehicle.	Date Aqd.	Notes.
YDW351	143	Guy Warrior articulated tractor unit	10.1961	
YDW356	195	Pacific drawbar tractor	9.1961	ex-WD; named - Challenger
YDW365		Ford Consul motor car	9.1961	Owned by Robert Wynn & Sons (Manchester) Ltd
YDW420	135	Guy Warrior articulated tractor unit	10.1961	
YDW421	136	Guy Warrior articulated tractor unit	10.1961	
996DNY	137	Guy Warrior flat lorry	1961	Dated from 1960, bought secondhand
YDW440	138	Bedford 7ton tipper	9.1961	
YDW441	139	Bedford 7ton tipper	9.1961	
YDW485	107	Guy Warrior articulated tractor unit	10.1961	
YDW486	108	Guy Warrior articulated tractor unit	10.1961	
DUH701	148	Thornycroft timber tractor	1961	ex-WD; no other details
YDW521	101	Guy Invincible 6wl articulated tractor unit	1961	
UUH62	102	Bedford 7ton flat lorry	1961	New in 1960, bought secondhand
759PPE	103	Bedford 7ton flat lorry	1961	New in 1960, bought secondhand
FWN919		Guy Invincible 8wl tipper	1961	Origins unknown, sold or broken up in same year
GER880		Ward LaFrance wrecker	1961	ex-WD; bought secondhand, possibly for spares
		Scammell Mountaineer drawbar Tractor	1961	Bought from Sunter Bros., Northallerton, possibly for spares or to rebuild
154AAX	63	Commer 7ton tipper	1961	New in 1960 to Star Brick & Tile Co. Ltd., Ponthir
WAX642	66	Seddon articulated tractor unit	1961	New in 1959 to Star Brick & Tile Co. Ltd., Ponthir
XWO305	70	Ford Thames Trader tipper	1961	New in 1960 to Star Brick & Tile Co. Ltd., Ponthir
XWO218	71	Ford Thames Trader tipper	1961	New in 1960 to Star Brick & Tile Co. Ltd., Ponthir
YDW522	178	Scammell Highwayman articulated tractor unit	1.1962	
YDW788		Ford Zodiac motor car	12.1962	Number transferred from DW27
YDW860		Austin A60 motor car	2.1962	

Index No.	Fleet No.	Vehicle.	Date Aqd.	Notes.
609DW		Scammell articulated tractor unit	3.1962	Date new not known; origins may have been the same as 610DW; owned by Black Diamond Transport Co., 187, Malpas Road, Newport; suspect that WYNNS had some involvement with the sale of the vehicle
610DW	94	Scammell articulated tractor unit	2.1962	Date new not known; bought unregistered from Michigan Plant
611DW	95	Guy Invincible articulated tractor unit	3.1962	
612DW	96	Guy Invincible articulated tractor unit	4.1962	
906DW	111	AEC Matador tackle wagon	4.1962	ex-WD; Owned by Wynns (Engineering) Ltd.;
1120DW		Ford Consul motor car	5.1962	
1121DW		Ford Consul motor car	5.1962	
1122DW		Ford Zephyr motor car	6.1962	Number transferred from TDW900
1300DW	90	Diamond T 980 drawbar tractor	10.1962	ex-WD; Owned by Robert Wynn & Sons (Manchester) Ltd
1428DW		Ford Anglia motor car	7.1962	
1430DW		Ford Anglia motor car	7.1962	
1443DW	115	AEC Matador tackle wagon	8.1962	ex-WD; Owned by Wynns (Engineering) Ltd
1474DW		Ford Anglia motor car	8.1962	
1505DW		Ford Anglia estate car	8.1962	
1506DW		Ford Anglia motor car	8.1962	Owned by Crindau Garages Ltd
1570DW	194	Pacific drawbar tractor	12.1962	ex-WD; named - Valiant
1664DW		Pacific drawbar tractor	10.1962	Registration by mistake - cancelled
1767DW		Ford Zodiac motor car	11.1962	Number transferred from DW110
1840DW		Vauxhall Victor motor car	11.1962	
1986DW		Jaguar Mk10 motor car	1.1963	Number transferred from RTV990
995ABO	6	Ford Thames 15cwt truck	1962	New in 1961, bought secondhand
2003DW	8	Ford Thames 12cwt truck	1962	May have been bought secondhand
2094DW		Guy Invincible 8wl flat lorry	1.1963	
2062DW		Guy 8wl lorry	1.1963	
2224DW		Ford Thames	4.1963	Owned by Crindau Garages Ltd.; model & type unknown

Index No.	Fleet No.	Vehicle.	Date Aqd.	Notes.
2656DW		Ford Anglia motor car	5.1963	
2932DW	7	Ford Trader	6.1963	Owned by Robert Wynn & Sons (Manchester) Ltd
3312DW	21	Drott bulldozer	8.1963	
3580DW	116	Bedford dropside lorry	10.1963	
3591DW	117	Bedford dropside lorry	11.1963	
3624DW	201	Ward LaFrance wrecker	10.1963	ex-WD
1321VP	207	Ross fork lift truck	1963	Dated from 1959; bought secondhand
3630DW	91	Diamond T drawbar tractor	10.1963	ex-WD; preserved.
3773DW		Ford Zodiac motor car	11.1963	
3789DW	169	Guy Invincible articulated tractor unit	1.1964	
3808DW	229	Bedford articulated tractor unit	1.1964	
4042DW		Rover motor car	1.1964	Number transferred from ODW888
4238DW		Ford Zephyr motor car	2.1964	Owned by Robert Wynn & Sons (Manchester) Ltd
4079DW		Jaguar 3.4 motor car	1.1964	Number transferred from DW27
4333DW		Ford Zephyr 4 motor car	2.1964	
4343DW		Ford Zephyr 4 motor car	2.1964	
4527DW		Morris 1100 motor car	3.1964	Number transferred from 1428DW
4551DW		Ford Zodiac motor car	3.1964	Number transferred from TDW900
5014DW		Diamond T drawbar tractor	5.1964	Mistaken registration - cancelled
5060DW		MG 1100 motor car	5.1964	Owned by N.R. Wynn
5126DW		Morris 1100 motor car	6.1964	Owned by H.P. Wynn
5335DW		Mercedez Benz motor car	5.1965	Number transferred from RTW370
5336DW		Jaguar motor car	5.1965	Number transferred from RTV990
5343DW		Ford Zodiac motor car	2.1966	Number transferred from DW110
5366DW		Landrover	12.1968	Number transferred from, DW31
ADW116B	205	Allen mobile crane	7.1964	Owned by Wynns (Engineering) Ltd
ADW228B	197	Pacific drawbar tractor	7.1964	ex-WD; named - Enterprise; preserved by Mike Lawrence, Somerset. He also has the 1890 built 40 ton boiler wagon.
ADW298B	123	Bedford articulated tractor unit	7.1964	
ADW299B	124	Bedford articulated tractor unit	9.1964	

Scammell Highwayman low-loader YDW522 (178) leads another, both loaded with dump trucks.

Looking all the world like a Bedford, YDW22 (216) was infact a rebuilt ex-WD AEC Matador tackle wagon, but fitted with a Bedford cab. Operated without badging the truck was owned by Wynns (Engineering) Ltd.

Electrical equipment loaded on four WYNNS outfits, one of the trailers of which was specially designed to carry loads in slung position. From the left: Guy YDW421 (136), Commer ODW479 (259), Guy YDW351 (143) and Bedford LDW835 (235).

Pacific drawbar tractor 1570DW (194) pauses in the snow. Shown are mates Peter Collier and Jimmy Doyle. Driver Roger Banfield took the photograph.

Pacific drawbar tractor, index number: YDW356 (195) - Challenger.

Pacific drawbar tractor ADW228B (197), the sixth and last of its type to enter service is shown disembarking from a RO/RO ship.

Index No.	Fleet No.	Vehicle.	Date Aqd.	Notes.
ADW300B	125	Bedford articulated tractor unit	1964	
ADW301B	129	Bedford articulated tractor unit	9.1964	
ADW703B	55	Bedford 8ton tipper	9.1964	
ADW723B	56	Bedford 8ton tipper	9.1964	
ADW869B	57	Bedford 8ton tipper	10.1964	
ADW870B	58	Bedford 8ton tipper	10.1964	
ADW910B	59	Bedford 8ton tipper	10.1964	
ADW911B	60	Bedford 8ton tipper	10.1964	
ADW947B		Ford Zephyr 6 motor car	10.1964	
BDW42B	206	Hydrocon Highlander mobile crane	10.1964	Owned by Wynns (Engineering) Ltd
BDW114B	61	Bedford 8ton tipper	11.1964	
BDW123B		Ford Zephyr motor car	11.1964	
BDW140B	270	Iron Fairy crane	11.1964	Owned by Wynns (Engineering) Ltd; 1982 transferred to Wynns Heavy Haulage, Stafford
BDW184B	9	Bedford pickup	11.1964	
BDW185B	62	Bedford 8ton tipper	11.1964	
BDW186B	127	Bedford articulated tractor unit	11.1964	
BDW219B	241	AEC Matador tackle wagon	11.1964	ex-WD; owned by Wynns (Engineering) Ltd
BDW277B	249	Diamond T 980 drawbar tractor	12.1964	ex-WD
BDW291B	231	AEC Matador tackle wagon	1964	ex-WD
BDW332B	46	Bedford 8ton tipper	12.1964	
BDW367C	217	AEC Matador tackle wagon	1.1965	ex-WD; Owned by Wynns (Engineering) Ltd
BDW371C	121	Atkinson articulated tractor unit	1.1965	
BDW372C	122	Atkinson articulated tractor unit	1.1965	
BDW381C	47	Bedford 8ton tipper	1.1965	
BDW382C	48	Bedford 8ton tipper	1.1965	
BDW383C	49	Bedford 8ton tipper	1.1965	
BDW384C	50	Bedford 5ton tipper	1.1965	
BDW385C	10	Bedford pickup	1.1965	Owned by Crindau Garages Ltd

Index No.	Fleet No.	Vehicle.	Date Aqd.	Notes.
BDW435B		Jaguar 3.4 motor car	11.1965	Number transferred from DW27
BDW442B		Rover motor car	4.1969	Number transferred from ODW888; owned by O.G. Wynn
BDW485C	51	Bedford 8ton tipper	1.1965	
BDW486C	52	Bedford 5ton tipper	3.1965	
BDW487C	53	Bedford 8ton tipper	3.1965	
BDW488C	144	Scammell Highwayman articulated tractor unit	1.1965	
BDW489C	145	Scammell Highwayman articulated tractor unit	3.1965	
BDW490C	146	Scammell Highwayman articulated tractor unit	7.1965	
BDW491C	147	Scammell Highwayman articulated tractor unit	6.1965	
BDW887C	130	Bedford articulated tractor unit	3.1965	
6686MW	119	Atkinson articulated tractor unit	1965	New in 1962 to Bulwark (Contracts) Ltd., operating on steel contract out of Llanwern Steelworks

Author's Note:

When the Spencer Steelworks of Richard Thomas and Baldwin Ltd (RTB) at Llanwern opened in 1962 Bulwark Transport of Chippenham were awarded the external transport contract through their subsidiary - Bulwark (Contracts) Ltd. Although other hauliers were used on Open 'A' carriers licences, the Bulwark vehicles were on contract licences restricting them to carry for RTB alone. They initially put a large number of Atkinson four wheel articulated tractor units usually connected to Duramin four in line semi-trailers on the contract. Later Seddon tractor units were added to this fleet.

Bulwark was part of the United Transport Group founded by the Watts family of Lydney, in the Forest of Dean, and had large holdings in passenger transport in Africa, particularly in Kenya, Tanzania and Uganda, and in 1964 acquired Robert Wynn & Sons Ltd. Their bus business in the UK - Red & White had been nationalised by the Atlee Government in the late 1940s. The registered office of this group was at Chepstow, Monmouthshire. The name Bulwark is taken from that area of Chepstow, where Red & White's headquarters had been.

The Atkinson tractor unit, index number: 6686MW which dated from 1962 and was acquired in 1965 is of special interest to me, as I had dealt with an insecure load involving the vehicle in 1964, when as a young Policeman of less than a years service it had dropped a steel coil on the road on a severe bend (now a lay-by) on the A465 Abergavenny to Hereford Road a mile or so North of Pandy, and it took hours before the mobile crane arrived to reload it.

The driver subsequently appeared before Cross Ash Magistrates' Court on one of its monthly Saturday morning sittings, pleaded guilty, and was fined. I cannot remember the amount of his fine, but I never forget a vehicle.

6694MW	120	Atkinson articulated tractor unit	1965	New in 1962 to Bulwark (Contracts) Ltd., operating on steel contract out of Llanwern Steelworks
CJ4528		Aveling Porter steam road roller	c1965	No details

Index No.	Fleet No.	Vehicle.	Date Aqd.	Notes.
L8965		Aveling Porter steam road roller	c1965	No details
CDW204C	131	Bedford articulated tractor unit	1965	
CDW281C	54	Bedford 8ton tipper	4.1965	
CDW293C		Morris 1100 motor car	3.1965	
CDW342C	236	Guy Invincible articulated tractor unit	5.1965	
CDW343C		Bedford articulated tractor unit	4.1965	
CDW381C	237	Guy Invincible articulated tractor unit	5.1965	
CDW475C	155	Bedford flat lorry	4.1965	
CDW577C	238	Guy Invincible articulated tractor unit	6.1965	
CDW865C	134	Bedford articulated tractor unit	7.1965	
CDW948C	239	Guy Invincible articulated tractor unit	7.1965	
DDW39C	274	Coles mobile crane	6.1965	Owned by Wynns (Engineering) Ltd
DDW111C	154	Bedford flat lorry	8.1965	
DDW255C	148	Scammell Highwayman articulated tractor unit	8.1965	
DDW362C	173	Bedford articulated tractor unit	8.1965	
DDW403C	240	Guy Invincible articulated tractor unit	10.1965	
DDW482C	235	Guy Invincible articulated tractor unit	11.1965	
DDW484C	234	Guy Invincible articulated tractor unit	10.1965	
DDW550C	149	Scammell Highwayman articulated tractor unit	11.1965	
DDW551C	233	Guy Invincible articulated tractor unit	10.1965	
DDW624C	232	Guy Invincible articulated tractor unit	11.1965	
EDW1D	218	AEC Mammoth Major 6wl articulated tractor unit	2.1966	
EDW292C		Jaguar 3.8 motor car	5.1968	Number transferred from DW27
EDW342D	151	Bedford flat lorry	3.1966	
EDW357D	225	Guy Big J articulated tractor unit	3.1966	
EDW399D	170	Seddon articulated tractor unit	2.1966	
EDW400D	171	Seddon articulated tractor unit	2.1966	
EDW409D		Ford Zephyr 4 motor car	2.1966	
EDW410D		Ford Zephyr 4 motor car	2.1966	

Index No.	Fleet No.	Vehicle.	Date Aqd.	Notes.
EDW411D		Ford Zephyr 4 motor car	4.1966	
EDW412D		Ford Zephyr motor car	2.1966	
EDW413D		Ford Zephyr 6 motor car	2.1966	
EDW414D	176	Scammell Highwayman articulated tractor unit	9.1966	
EDW782D	250	Diamond T drawbar tractor	3.1966	ex-WD
FDW91D	150	Bedford flat lorry	4.1966	
FDW124D	224	Guy Big J articulated tractor unit	5.1966	
FDW206D	223	Guy Big J articulated tractor unit	6.1966	
FDW300D		Ford Zodiac motor car	4.1966	
FDW333D		Ford Zodiac motor car	4.1966	
FDW375D	165	Bedford flat lorry	5.1966	
FDW536D	164	Albion Clydesdale flat lorry	6.1966	
FDW636D	215	Scammell wrecker	6.1966	Rebuilt by WYNNS; looked more like an AEC Matador than the Scammell whose badging it displayed
FDW706D		Morris 1100 motor car	6.1966	
FDW731D	177	Scammell Handyman articulated tractor unit	7.1966	
FDW769E	188	Scammell Contractor 100ton drawbar tractor	2.1967	Originally allocated the number FDW769D, but when not used in 1966 - 'E' suffix substituted; sometimes operated as an articulated tractor unit
FDW794D		Morris 1100 motor car	7.1966	Owned by H.P. Wynn
FDW900D		Morris 1100 motor car	7.1966	Owned by J. Wynn
GDW13D	275	Hydrocon Huntley mobile crane	9.1966	
GDW231D	189	Scammell Contractor 100ton drawbar tractor	11.1966	Sometimes operated as an articulated tractor unit
	109	Clarkter Yard Tug	c.1966	No other details
	110	Clarkter Yard Tug	c.1966	No other details

Author's Note:

In the Spring of 1969 the author, serving as a Police motor cyclist with the Gwent Constabulary Traffic Department at Police Headquarters, Abergavenny, commenced the escort of a WYNNS abnormal load from the Bus Station at Abergavenny, where it had been parked overnight. The load was a steel vessel (or tank) strung between two bogies and towed by a Diamond T drawbar tractor, index number: 1300DW (fleet no: 90) driven by Billy Wade from Usk. It was enroute from Cheshire to Cardiff Gas Works, and was routed along the A4042 Abergavenny to Newport Road. It was the first of over a dozen loads to be transported to this destination over the next month or so. (Not as stated in the press report). Mr Wadeand the author had known each other for a number of years as I had been a motor cyclist for over four years. On arrival at the roundabout outside Abergavenny, another abnormal load was waiting to be escorted over the same route. This being a lightweight BMC articulated outfit with a very light fibreglass swimming pool. This vehicle tagged on behind the slowish moving WYNNS vehicle.

On arrival at the bottom of the Horse & Jockey Pitch, near Pontypool, whilst the WYNNS load started the climb of the hill, the driver of the BMC vehicle was advised to wait in the lay-by at the bottom and not to proceed until the heavier vehicle had completed the climb. I went to the top of the hill and called following traffic past as the outfit made its climb. Normal procedure for the escorting officer. When about three-quarters of its way up the hill the hawser securing the metal tank to the front bogie parted and it fell off the bogie and ran back down the hill a short distance before coming to rest on the kerb and against a hedge. The following photographs tell their own story.

The matter did not rest there, as the report in the South Wales
Argus of Thursday, July 17, 1969 shows: -

His foresight averted serious accident

A police officer's foresight in stopping traffic following a heavily loaded double-trailer up a steep hill prevented disastrous consequences, Pontypool magistrates were told on Thursday.

The rear trailer, carrying a 35-ton load, became detached and ran back down the Horse and Jockey pitch near Pontypool and landed in a hedge, said Mr. Robin Mc-Ouat, prosecuting.

'One can imagine what disastrous consequences there would have been, had there been cars behind," he said.

Police-constable Paul Heaton, of the traffic department at Abergavenny, was commended by the magistrates for his foresight.

Stopped

Before the trailer started up the hill he stopped the traffic behind it and the drivers waited at the bottom.

The owners of the trailer, Robert Wynn and Sons Ltd., of Albany Street, Newport, and the driver, William Cyril Wade, 41, of Mill Street, Usk, pleaded guilty to using a vehicle carrying a load which was not so secured that danger was not likely to be caused.

The firm were fined £25 and Wade £5.

Mr. Gilbert Davies, defending, said the load was the 18th of its kind carried by the firm from Cheshire to Cardiff Gas Works.

Locked

The vehicle was travelling up the hill at two to three miles an hour when for some reason the emergency brakes acted on the rear trailer and locked it dead.

This threw terrific strain on the metal hawser securing the load and it broke. The airline snapped, releasing the air from the rear brakes, and the trailer and load rolled backwards.

Mr. Davies said that no matter what care was exercised in the loading and driving of the vehicles that type of accident could happen.

The firm were probably the largest haulage contractors in the country and used the best possible equipment. They accepted full responsibility and laid no blame upon the driver.

It wasn't long after the insecure load on the Jockey Pitch, that the second of these loads turned up on the County boundary at Dixton, Monmouth, and I duly commenced the escort along the A40 Monmouth to Abergavenny Road. On this occasion it was also on a set of two bogies, but under the charge of a 100ton Scammell Contractor GDW231D driven by Ian Trick. All went well, and on arrival at the Hardwick roundabout on the outskirts of Abergavenny the outfit turned left and joined the A4042 road towards Newport. After a mile or so we came to the humpbacked bridge over the River Usk at Llanellen, and as the vehicle went over, the hawsers securing the tank to the front bogie parted and the load shifted. The tractor unit had pulled the bogie forward from the position at which it was secured to its load, but fortunately it did not come off. After chocking the rear bogie so that it could not go back, the front bogie was pushed back to its original position and the whole lot re-secured. After about two hours the journey resumed, happily without further incident, and for Ian Trick without a summons.

Therefore the original damage must have been done to Billy Wade's load at this location. His hawsers had not parted, but must have stretched, slackening off the securing of the load.

This was the stuff of which fame is made. I can think of many cases in thirty years service where I deserved a pat on the back, but I never considered the Jockey Pitch incident to be one of them.

(Above): Wynns Engineering's AEC Matador tackle wagon BDW219B (241).

(Below): This Allen mobile crane ADW116B (205) was owned by Wynns (Engineering) Ltd.
It held the distinction of being the first WYNNS vehicle to carry the new registration system, ie the first 'B' reg.

This Ward LaFrance wrecker 3624DW (201) was one of seven of this ex-WD type to be registered by WYNNS in the twenty years from 1947.

The last Diamond T to enter the fleet was EDW782D (250) in March, 1966. Seen fitted with an Anderson cab, designed in-house. In all WYNNS had operated twenty-two of these extremely useful vehicles, with a gap between first and last of some nineteen years. I believe that some had been the subject of a rebuild with re-registration. It is known that up to three Diamond Ts carried out a contract in Spain in the late 1950s and were sold locally, but which vehicles I cannot identify. WYNNS were also known to have used Diamond T chassis' stripped down and modified as steerable bogies.

Author's Note:

You would imagine that Police Officers are quite sensible. Alas, that is not always the case. I became a motor cyclist at Abergavenny at the end of 1964. Although Llanwern Steelworks had been open for two years, industrial development was booming in South Wales, and there was a lot of wide, high, long and heavy loads needing escort through the area. Having spent four days (parking at night, of course) with a Pickfords load from Skenfrith to Abergavenny, and taking out the window of the Electricity Board Showroom, and the Great George Hotel's guttering at the same time on the final lap, I knew the frustrations of the job. But when escorting a load on that narrow stretch of the A40 between Hardwick roundabout near Abergavenny and Raglan roundabout, exactly eight miles we let it rip. When travelling towards Raglan there is a fairly moderate gradient at Parc Lettice and a steeper one at Clytha Cutting. Going the other way there is a moderate and short gradient coming out of Raglan and another at Aberffrwd and Parc Lettice. But caution has to be taken going downhill at Clytha. However in true formula one fashion the record for a 100ton plus gross outfit with a tractor at front and back towards Raglan is 21 minutes at an average speed of 23.75 mph, and towards Abergavenny 19 minutes averaging 26.25 mph. The vehicle - Scammell Contractor 100ton drawbar tractor GDW231D at the front. The driver - Ian Trick from Newport; in both directions. Never to be beaten, I know because I was there.

I do remember, but will not identify the driver, who was travelling towards Raglan and fell asleep at the wheel near Bryngwyn, and took the porch off the only house on the roadside for over three miles. It was a Scammell Contractor, and yes the driver did get a summons.

Index No.	Fleet No.	Vehicle.	Date Aqd.	Notes.
GDW249E	190	Scammell Contractor 100ton drawbar tractor	1.1967	
GDW271D		Ford Cortina motor car	10.1966	
GDW347E	113	AEC Matador tackle wagon	1.1967	ex-WD
GDW348D	114	AEC Matador tackle wagon	5.1966	ex-WD
GDW349E	267	Ward LaFrance wrecker	7.1967	ex-WD
GDW411D		Morris Mini Minor motor car	11.1966	Owned by H.P. Wynn
GDW539D		Ford motor car	1.1969	Number transferred from DW110
GDW765E	222	Guy Big J articulated tractor unit	3.1967	
GDW848E	186	Scammell Contractor 100ton drawbar tractor	4.1967	
GDW896E	2	Bedford minibus	3.1967	
GDW956E	140	Scammell Handyman articulated tractor unit	3.1967	
GDW958E	141	Scammell Handyman articulated tractor unit	3.1967	
HDW78E	251	Scammell Trunker articulated tractor unit	4.1967	
HDW100E		Ford Cortina motor car	3.1967	Owned by J. Wynn
HDW370E	126	Bedford articulated tractor unit	6.1967	
HDW371E	128	Bedford articulated tractor unit	6.1967	
HDW710F	102	Bedford articulated tractor unit	9.1967	

Index No.	Fleet No.	Vehicle.	Date Aqd.	Notes.
HDW711F	103	Bedford articulated tractor unit	9.1967	
JDW142F	63	Seddon articulated tractor unit	8.1967	
JDW146F	64	Seddon articulated tractor unit	8.1967	
HHR953F	65	Seddon articulated tractor unit	1967	New in 1967 to Bulwark Transport and transferred almost immediately to WYNNS
JDW147F	185	Scammell Contractor 150ton drawbar tractor	9.1967	Sometimes operated as an articulated tractor unit; late 1970s used in Sudan as an artic. At end of contract disposed of locally; named - Adventurer
JDW247F	183	Scammell Contractor 150ton drawbar tractor	9.1967	Sometimes operated as an articulated tractor unit; late 1970s used in Sudan as an artic. Do not believe that vehicle was brought back to UK at end of contract; named - Traveller
JDW369F	104	Bedford articulated tractor unit	9.1967	
JDW370F	45	Bedford tipper	9.1967	
JDW433F	105	Bedford articulated tractor unit	1967	
JDW652F	44	Bedford tipper	11.1967	
JDW749F	106	Bedford articulated tractor unit	1.1968	
KDW145F	159	Bedford 6ton flat lorry	2.1968	
KDW206F	252	Scammell Trunker articulated tractor unit	1.1968	
KDW278F	253	Scammell Trunker articulated tractor unit	1.1968	
KDW279F	254	Scammell Trunker articulated tractor unit	1.1968	
KDW350F	255	Scammell Trunker articulated tractor unit	2.1968	
KDW368F		Morris Minor motor car	1.1968	Owned by N.R. Wynn
KDW439F	12	Ford 3ton truck	2.1968	
KDW548F		Ford Cortina motor car	2.1968	
KDW549F		Ford Cortina motor car	2.1968	
KDW551F		Ford Cortina motor car	2.1968	
KDW552F		Ford Cortina motor car	2.1968	
KDW553F		Ford Cortina motor car	2.1968	

Index No.	Fleet No.	Vehicle.	Date Aqd.	Notes.
KDW554F		Ford Zephyr motor car	2.1968	
KDW555F		Ford Zodiac motor car	4.1968	
KDW585F		Ford Zodiac motor car	3.1968	
KDW588F	298	Ford D1000 articulated tractor unit	1968	On hire before purchase
KDW786F	84	AEC Mammoth Major 6wl articulated tractor unit	5.1968	Also used as a drawbar tractor
KDW787G	85	AEC Mammoth Major 6wl articulated tractor unit	9.1968	Also used as a drawbar tractor
KDW918F	256	Scammell Trunker articulated tractor unit	5.1968	
KDW963F		Morris 1100 motor car	3.1968	Owned by H.P. Wynn
LDW217F	268	Coles Hydra mobile crane	5.1968	Transferred in 1982 to Wynns Heavy Haulage, Stafford
LDW608G	213	AEC Matador tackle wagon	9.1968	ex-WD
LDW609F		AEC Matador tackle wagon	1968	Mistaken registration- cancelled
LDW947F		Jaguar motor car	5.1970	Number transferred from RTV990
LDW951F		Daimler motor car	1.1971	Number transferred from DW27
MDW419G	219	Scammell Handyman articulated tractor unit	12.1968	
MDW420G	220	Scammell Handyman articulated tractor unit	12.1968	
MDW421G	221	Scammell Handyman articulated tractor unit	12.1968	
MDW786G		Ford Escort motor car	12.1968	
MDW789G		MGB GT motor car	12.1968	Owned by R.O.J. Wynn
NDW10G		Rover 2000 motor car	1.1969	
NDW12G	263	Coles mobile crane	1.1969	Transferred in 1982 to Wynns Heavy Haulage, Stafford
NDW187G		Guy Big J articulated tractor unit	3.1969	
NDW188G	228	Guy Big J articulated tractor unit	3.1969	
NDW345G	192	Pacific drawbar tractor	3.1969	re-build of GDW277 (1950) using Scammell parts; named - Dreadnought
NDW382G		Ford Cortina motor car	3.1969	
NDW591H	86	AEC Mammoth Major 6wl articulated tractor unit	9.1969	

Index No.	Fleet No.	Vehicle.	Date Aqd.	Notes.
NDW592G	87	AEC Mammoth Major 6wl articulated tractor unit	7.1969	
NDW832G	227	Guy Big J articulated tractor unit	5.1969	
NDW764G	269	Iron Fairy mobile crane	1969	Transferred in 1982 to Wynns Heavy Haulage, Stafford
NDW836G	182	Scammell Contractor 240ton drawbar tractor	6.1969	In the late 1970s used in the Sudan as an articulated tractor unit; out of the fleet by 1982, believed left in Africa; named - Conqueror
NDW837G	184	Scammell Contractor 240ton drawbar tractor	6.1969	Transferred in 1982 to Wynns Heavy Haulage, Stafford; named - Challenger
NDW838H	187	Scammell Contractor 240ton drawbar tractor	10.1969	Used in the mid 1970s on Tanzania/Zambia contract later refurbished in Kenya and stayed working there; sold locally; Still in service; re-engined in 2002. Named - Supreme.
NDW839H	191	Scammell Contractor 240ton drawbar tractor	8.1969	Used in the mid 1970s on Tanzania/Zambia contract later refurbished in Kenya and stayed working there; sold locally; still in service. Named - Crusader
NDW872G		Ford Cortina motor car	5.1969	
NDW996G		BMC motor car	6.1969	
ODW131G	66	Guy Big J articulated tractor unit	7.1969	
ODW132G	67	Guy Big J articulated tractor unit	7.1969	
ODW133G	68	Guy Big J articulated tractor unit	7.1969	
ODW134G	69	Guy Big J articulated tractor unit	7.1969	
ODW135G	70	Guy Big J articulated tractor unit	7.1969	
ODW528G		Morris motor car	1.1973	Number transferred from DW110; owned by H.P. Wynn
ODW686G		Ford Cortina motor car	8.1969	
ODW800H	14	Morris J2 van	10.1969	
ODW815H	71	Guy Big J articulated tractor unit	10.1969	
ODW888H		Sunbeam Imp motor car	10.1969	Owned by J. Wynn
PDW36H	26	Ford Transit pickup	1969	
PDW285H		Hillman Minx motor car	12.1969	

Index No.	Fleet No.	Vehicle.	Date Aqd.	Notes.
PDW433H		Ford Escort motor car	1.1970	
PDW441H	175	Scammell Handyman articulated tractor unit	3.1970	
PDW721H		Triumph 1300 motor car	2.1970	
PDW855H		Austin 3 litre motor car	2.1970	
PDW888H		Ford Escort motor car	3.1970	
RDW219H		Vauxhall Victor motor car	4.1970	
RDW348H	16	Ford Transit van	4.1970	
RDW349H	15	Ford Transit pickup	4.1970	
RDW457H		Ford Transit pickup	5.1970	
RDW458H		Ford Transit pickup	5.1970	
RDW586H		Morris Mini Clubman estate car	5.1970	
RDW624H	72	Guy Big J articulated tractor unit	6.1970	
RDW625H	73	Guy Big J articulated tractor unit	6.1970	
RDW626H		Guy Big J articulated tractor unit	6.1970	
RDW639H		Guy Big J articulated tractor unit	7.1970	
RDW871J	74	Guy Big J articulated tractor unit	8.1970	
SDW110J	75	Guy Big J articulated tractor unit	9.1970	
SDW246J		Triumph motor car	8.1970	
SDW543J		Ford Cortina 1600 motor car	9.1970	
SDW545J	198	Scammell Contractor 150ton drawbar tractor	10.1970	Used in mid 1970s on a contract in Nigeria; local index no: LAE2087; no other details
SDW937J	200	Scammell Contractor 150ton drawbar tractor	11.1970	Sometimes used as an articulated tractor unit
SDW948J	112	AEC Matador tackle wagon	11.1970	ex-WD
TDW83J	280	Scammell Contractor 150ton drawbar tractor	2.1971	Used in the late 1970s on a contract in the Sudan; no evidence of return to UK
TDW84J	76	Guy Big J articulated tractor unit	12.1970	
TDW230J		Ford Escort motor car	11.1970	
UDW139J	281	Scammell Contractor 150ton drawbar tractor	6.1971	Used in mid 1970s on a contract in Nigeria; local index no: LAE2089; was sometimes used as an articulated tractor unit; no other details

Index No.	Fleet No.	Vehicle.	Date Aqd.	Notes.
VDW606K		Daimler motor car	5.1974	Number transferred from RTV990
VDW939K		Morris 1000 motor car	9.1971	Owned by R.J. Wynn
WDW542K	111	AEC Matador tackle wagon	1971	ex-WD; preserved by Brian Griffiths, St Brides, Magor
WDW599K	18	Ford Transit van	11.1971	
XDW578K	92	Atkinson Venturer 6wl articulated tractor unit	4.1972	
XDW877K	93	Atkinson Venturer 6wl articulated tractor unit	6.1972	
XDW878K	94	Atkinson Venturer 6wl articulated Tractor unit	6.1972	Around 1980 converted to wrecker using the body & crane from Diamond T PDW321; transferred in 1982 to Wynns Heavy Haulage, Stafford; c1983 to Roberts - Ross Roadways, Whitchurch, Ross on Wye still as a wrecker; c2002 sold privately for preservation
CDW518L		Austin motor car	1.1973	Owned by H.P. Wynn
DDW812L	95	Atkinson Venturer articulated tractor unit	6.1973	
DDW813L	96	Atkinson Venturer articulated tractor unit	6.1973	
EDW296L	229	Atkinson Borderer articulated tractor unit	6.1973	
EDW480L	230	Atkinson Borderer articulated tractor unit	7.1973	
WDG463J	3	Ford Transit minibus	1973	New in 1972, bought secondhand
ODF599K	19	Ford Transit van	1973	New in 1972, bought secondhand
NDW52M	97	Atkinson Venturer 6wl articulated tractor unit	9.1973	
NDW53M	98	Atkinson Venturer 6wl articulated tractor unit	11.1973	Shipped out to the Sudan in 1980 to replace a worn out Bedford TM tractor unit; no evidence of return to the UK at end of contract
NDW246M		Triumph PI motor car	8.1973	
NDW261M	99	Atkinson Venturer 6wl articulated tractor unit	12.1973	
NDW721M		Ford Cortina motor car	8.1973	
ODW251M	231	Atkinson Borderer articulated tractor unit	11.1973	

Seen at Abersychan is Diamond T - 3630DW (91) hauling an excavator which had been loaded at Blaenersychan Colliery. The author, a Police motor cyclist, was the escorting officer.

Dating from November, 1965, this Scammell Highwayman articulated low-loader DDW550C (149) is seen at the Albany Street yard at Newport.

Since the firm of Robert Wynn & Sons Ltd had been absorbed into the United Transport Group in 1964 considerable investment had taken place in relation to various sections of the fleet. A new tipper fleet had been acquired, new vehicles for operation at the lower end of the heavy haulage fleet had arrived, and the general haulage fleet and tanker section had all received new vehicles. The timber extraction business had been disposed of partly due to the contraction in timber felling. At last in 1966 the long awaited investment in the heavy haulage fleet started to arrive. WYNNS had been involved with Scammell in the development of the Contractor range, favouring it over the Constructor and Super Constructor model. Commencing in 1966 right up to the transfer of the business to a new company at Stafford in 1982 a total of twenty-five Scammell Contractors entered the fleet, comprising of four of 100ton, six of 150ton, thirteen of 240ton and two of 250ton capacity, and although they are all included in the main fleet list, I will list them collectively hereunder:

Index No.	Fleet No.	Name.	Date Entered Service.	Capacity (tonnage).
FDW769E	188	-	2.1967	100
GDW231D	189	-	11.1966	100
GDW249E	190	-	1.1967	100
GDW848E	186	-	4.1967	100
JDW147F	185	Adventurer	9.1967	150
JDW247F	183	Traveller	9.1967	150
NDW836G	182	Conqueror	6.1969	240
NDW837G	184	Challenger	6.1969	240
NDW838H	187	Supreme	10.1969	240
NDW839H	191	Crusader	8.1969	240
SDW545J	198	-	10.1970	150
SDW937J	200	-	11.1970	150
TDW83J	280	-	2.1971	150
UDW139J	281	-	6.1971	150
RDW339M	193	Hercules	7.1974	240
SDW173N	194	Champion	8.1974	240
GTX211N	195	Resolute	1975	240
HHB361N	196	Talisman	1975	240
KAX395P	600	Renown	1976	240
RWO73R	602	Superior	1977	250 (Mk2)
OBO3R	604	Illustrious	1977	240
XAX512T	628	Cavalier	1979	240
YAX165T	631	Buccaneer	1979	240
YWO24T	633	Musketeer	1979	240
DBO661V	640	Invincible	1980	250 (Mk2)

© The Wynn's Preservation Group

What should have been the first Scammell Contractor 100ton drawbar tractor to enter service was FDW769E (188) intended to enter service in 1966, she had been allocated a 'D' registration but this was changed when the entry was delayed until February, 1967. In the event GDW231D registered in November, 1966 was the first into service. FDW769E is seen later in her career operating as an articulated tractor unit.

Shown in 1975 this hardworked Scammell Contractor GDW848E (186) was the fourth and last of the 100ton model.

Two views of the Scammell Contractor 150ton tractor JDW147F (185) but operating as an articulated outfit. This vehicle was shipped out to the Sudan in the late 1970s, and at the end of the contract was sold locally, possibly for scrap. The 100 ton and 150ton Contractors were not normally named, but for the Sudan contract 185 was named Adventurer.

Scammell Contractor JDW247F (183) was used in the Sudan in the late 1970s being named Traveller.
It is not known whether the vehicle returned to the UK or was disposed of in Africa, The lower view shows
it hard at work in the UK carrying a locomotive from Barry.

This Scammell Trunker 6x2 articulated tractor unit KDW279F (254) dating from January, 1968 was normally operated in the tanker fleet. It is being used here as a low-loader.

WYNNS held an agency for Guy Lorries through its subsidiary company - Crindau Garages Ltd. Not surprisingly they operated a large number of Guy vehicles. Seen here loaded with a section of prefabricated steelwork is Guy Big 'J' NDW832G (227) (above). The name Crindau, is taken from that area of Newport where the firm's headquarters was situated.

(Below): Operating as a low-loader, this Guy Big 'J' unit ODW134G (69) entered the fleet in July, 1969.

(Above): Two Guy Big 'J' tractor units - ODW131G (66) and RDW871J (74) looking somewhat forlorn.

(Below): The Guy Big 'J' articulated tractor unit ODW133G (68).

Dreadnought - the rebuilt Pacific NDW345G (192) is shown hauling a furnace 28ft high into Llanwern Steelworks. This was part of a consignment built in the North East which was shipped by sea to Newport and was transhipped to a pontoon which was taken upstream to the specially constructed Porton Wharf adjacent to the works. This wharf, which jutted out into the Bristol Channel, was removed following the shipments, and the shoreline re-instated as before.

Another view of Pacific NDW345G (192) , parked outside the Albany Street, Newport, depot

Index No.	Fleet No.	Vehicle.	Date Aqd.	Notes.
PDW794M	232	Atkinson Borderer articulated tractor unit	5.1974	
PDW878M	10	Ford Transit van	4.1974	
RDW339M	193	Scammell Contractor 240ton drawbar tractor	7.1974	Used on the Tanzania/Zambia contract in the mid 1970s; later returned to the UK and refurbished being converted to an articulated tractor unit, thereafter used in the Sudan in the late 1970s/ early 1980s; do not know if the vehicle was returned to the UK at contract end; Named - Hercules
RDW664N		Ford Escort motor car	8.1974	
RDW697M		Peugeot estate car	7.1974	Bought for use on the Tanzania/Zambia contract
RDW857N		Ford Cortina motor car	8.1974	
SDW164N		Ford Transit Caravanette	8.1974	Supplied by Crickhowell Caravans, Llanwenarth Citra, Near Abergavenny, for use on the Tanzania/ Zambia contract; at least one was later used in Kenya; no further details
SDW165N		Ford Transit Caravanette	8.1974	As at SDW164N
SDW166N		Ford Transit Caravanette	8.1974	As at SDW164N
SDW167N		Ford Transit Caravanette	8.1974	As at SDW164N
SDW168N		Ford Transit Caravanette	8.1974	As at SDW164N
SDW169N		Ford Transit Caravanette	8.1974	As at SDW164N
SDW173N	194	Scammell Contractor 240ton drawbar tractor	8.1974	Used on the Tanzania/ Zambia contract in the mid 1970s, thereafter returned to the UK, refurbished and converted to an articulated tractor unit; thereafter used in the late 1970s/early 1980s in the Sudan; do not know if the vehicle was returned to the UK at contract end; named - Champion
SDW492N		Ford Granada motor car	9.1974	
SDW568N		Atkinson articulated tractor unit	9.1974	
GTX211N	195	Scammell Contractor 240ton drawbar tractor	1975	Used in Nigeria from mid 1970s until at least 1980, thereafter returned to UK; transferred in 1982 to Wynns Heavy Haulage, Stafford; named - Resolute
HHB361N	196	Scammell Contractor 240ton drawbar tractor	1975	Used in the Sudan from late 1970s; do not know if returned to UK at contract end; Named - Talisman

Index No.	Fleet No.	Vehicle.	Date Aqd.	Notes.
GKG838N	233	Atkinson Borderer articulated tractor unit	1975	
GTG56N	234	Seddon articulated tractor unit	1975	
HAX685N	235	Seddon articulated tractor unit	1975	
HAX686N	236	Seddon articulated tractor unit	1975	
HBO595N	237	Seddon articulated tractor unit	1975	
HBO596N	238	Seddon articulated tractor unit	1975	
TTD174L	240	Seddon articulated tractor unit	1975	New in 1973 to John Ancliffe, Manchester
TTD175L	242	Seddon articulated tractor unit	1975	New in 1973 to John Ancliffe, Manchester
HBO753N	100	Atkinson Venturer 6wl articulated tractor unit	1975	
KTG582P	4	Ford Transit crewbus	1976	
KTG583P	20	Ford Transit van	1976	
KTX731P	245	ERF articulated tractor unit	1976	Transferred in 1982 to Industrial Fuels Transport, Avonmouth
KTX732P	246	ERF articulated tractor unit	1976	Transferred in 1982 to Industrial Fuels Transport, Avonmouth
KAX391P	243	Seddon-Atkinson articulated tractor Unit	1976	Transferred in 1982 to industrial Fuels Transport, Avonmouth
KAX392P	244	Seddon-Atkinson articulated tractor unit	1976	Transferred in 1982 to Industrial Fuels Transport, Avonmouth
KAX393P	16	Ford Transit pickup	1976	
KAX394P	17	Ford Transit pickup	1976	
KAX395P	600	Scammell Contractor 240ton drawbar tractor	1976	Usually operated as an articulated tractor unit. Transferred in 1982 to Wynns Heavy Haulage, Stafford; Named - Renown; preserved by Graham Booth, Southport
KAX396P	603	Scania 6wl articulated tractor unit	1976	Transferred in 1982 to Wynns Heavy Haulage, Stafford
LDW340P	601	ERF articulated tractor unit	1976	Transferred in 1982 to Industrial Fuel Transport, Avonmouth
PHB304R	605	ERF articulated tractor unit	1976	Transferred in 1982 to Industrial Fuel Transport, Avonmouth

Index No.	Fleet No.	Vehicle.	Date Aqd.	Notes.
RWO73R	602	Scammell Contractor 250ton drawbar tractor	1977	This vehicle was the prototype of Scammell's Mk 2 Contractor of which only six were built; WYNNS had two - the other being DBO661V (1980). See later, Pickfords had two and the other two went to Wynns Heavy Haulage, Stafford in 1983. RWO73R was transferred in 1982 to Wynns Heavy Haulage, Stafford thence United Heavy Haulage, and Econofreight United Heavy Haulage, from whom in 2001 vehicle was acquired by Robert Willson, Pontypool, and preserved; named - Superior
OBO3R	604	Scammell Contractor 240ton drawbar tractor	1977	I believe that this number was allocated to this vehicle but suspect that it was never licensed in the UK, as on delivery it was shipped out to work in Nigeria. Local registration number LA4668; I can find no evidence that it ever returned to the UK. A number of Contractors worked in the African continent and were disposed of at the end of contracts locally, others were shipped back to the UK. Named - Illustrious
	608	Bedford MK mobile workshop	1977	Acquired for use in the Sudan; I believe at the end of contract it was disposed of locally; It was never registered in the UK, but carried an Arabic index number
	609	Bedford TM 6wl articulated tractor unit	1977	As for 608
	610	Bedford TM 6wl articulated tractor unit	1977	As for 608
	611	Bedford TM 6wl articulated tractor unit	1977	As for 608
	612	Bedford MK mobile kitchen	1977	As for 608
VMW256K	606	Seddon articulated tractor unit	1977	New in 1972 to Bulwark Transport, Chippenham
VMW257K	607	Seddon articulated tractor unit	1977	New in 1972 to Bulwark Transport, Chippenham
RKG105R	614	Ford Transit van	1977	
RTX64R	613	ERF articulated tractor unit	1977	Transferred in 1982 to Industrial Fuel Transport, Avonmouth
RTX65R	615	ERF articulated tractor unit	1977	Transferred in 1982 to Industrial Fuel Transport, Avonmouth
SUH824S	616	ERF articulated tractor unit	1977	Transferred in 1982 to Industrial Fuel Transport, Avonmouth

Index No.	Fleet No.	Vehicle.	Date Aqd.	Notes.
SWO389S	617	Ford Transit van	1977	Transferred in 1982 to Wynns Heavy Haulage, Stafford
AAX542T	618	Volvo F89 articulated tractor unit	1978	Acquired in 1977 and stored; transferred in 1982 to Wynns Heavy Haulage, Stafford
ABO421T	619	Volvo F89 articulated tractor unit	1978	Acquired in 1977 and stored; transferred in 1982 to Wynns Heavy Haulage, Stafford
TDW297S	620	ERF articulated tractor unit	1978	Transferred in 1982 to Industrial Fuel Transport, Avonmouth
TDW298S	621	ERF articulated tractor unit	1978	Transferred in 1982 to Industrial Fuel Transport, Avonmouth
UTX663S	622	ERF articulated tractor unit	1978	Transferred in 1982 to Industrial Fuel Transport, Avonmouth
UTG621S	623	ERF articulated tractor unit	1978	Transferred in 1982 to Industrial Fuel Transport, Avonmouth
TTX633S	624	ERF articulated tractor unit	1978	Transferred in 1982 to Wynns Heavy Haulage, Stafford
TWO470S	625	Bedford KM dropside lorry	1978	Tackle wagon fitted with HIAB crane; transferred in 1982 to Wynns Heavy Haulage, Stafford
VTG193S	629	Bedford KM dropside lorry	1978	Tackle wagon fitted with HIAB crane; transferred in 1982 to Wynns Heavy Haulage, Stafford
VUH713S	626	Scammell Amazon 6wl 100ton articulated tractor unit	1979	Transferred in 1982 to Wynns Heavy Haulage, Stafford
YGS384S	627	Scammell Amazon 6wl 100ton articulated tractor unit	1979	Transferred in 1982 to Wynns Heavy Haulage, Stafford
XTG945T	630	Landrover	1977	Bought in kit form in Kenya and assembled for the Sudan contract; at conclusion shipped to UK and registered
		Landrover	1977	Bought in kit form in Kenya and assembled for the Sudan contract, sold locally at contract end
XAX512T	628	Scammell Contractor 240ton drawbar tractor	1979	Transferred in 1982 to Wynns Heavy Haulage, Stafford; Named - Cavalier

An early 240ton Scammell Contractor drawbar tractor NDW837G (184) shown at the
Albany Street, Newport headquarters of Robert Wynn & Sons Ltd.

© The Wynn's Preservation Group

The transportation of railway locomotives from the Woodham Bros. Scrapyard at Barry, South Glamorgan,
on behalf of various preservation groups was an important area of business for the firm. Scammell NDW839H
(191) is shown carrying out such a job. This vehicle and its sister Contractor NDW838H (187) survive in Kenya,
and are still very much in service.

This Egromatic-cabbed AEC Mammoth Major 6x4 articulated tractor unit
KDW787G (85) was one of four of this type acquired in the late 1960s.

Two AEC Matador tackle wagons (above) SDW948J (112) registered in 1970, and (below) WDW542K (111) which entered service in 1971. This vehicle is preserved by Brian Griffiths of St. Brides, Monmouthshire.

This Egromatic-cabbed AEC Mammoth Major 6x4 articulated tractor unit
KDW787G (85) was one of four of this type acquired in the late 1960s.

Two AEC Matador tackle wagons (above) SDW948J (112) registered in 1970, and (below) WDW542K (111) which entered service in 1971. This vehicle is preserved by Brian Griffiths of St. Brides, Monmouthshire.

Scammell Contractor 150ton drawbar tractor SDW545J (198) (above) with a pre-cast beam and (below) being washed down at the Manchester depot by Max Williams.

Scammell Contractor UDW139J (281), (above) edging slowly forward under a railway bridge, and (below) at rest.

Two 1973 Atkinson Venturer articulated tractor units (above) XDW578K (92) and (below) XDW877K (93).

(Overleaf):A striking view of Atkinson Venturer articulated tractor unit, index no: XDW878K (94) which entered service in June, 1972. In 1980 it was converted to a wrecker using the body and crane from Diamond T - PDW321. Passing to Wynns Heavy Haulage, Stafford in 1982, it was soon sold to Ross Roadways (Roberts Brothers) at Whitchurch, Ross on Wye, who have recently disposed of it for preservation.

This Atkinson Venturer articulated tractor unit NDW53M (98) was one of nine owned by the firm. It was shipped out to the Sudan in 1980 to replace a Bedford TM which had been sold locally. I can find no trace that the vehicle returned to the UK at the end of the contract, and assume that it was also sold locally.

EDW296L (229) was an Atkinson Borderer tractor unit which was normally used in the heavy haulage fleet.

Index No.	Fleet No.	Vehicle.	Date Aqd.	Notes.
YAX165T	631	Scammell Contractor 240ton drawbar tractor	1979	Transferred in 1980 to Wrekin Roadways, Telford; transferred in 1982 to Wynns Heavy Haulage, Stafford; named - Buccaneer
YWO24T	633	Scammell Contractor 240ton drawbar tractor	1979	Transferred in 1982 to Wynns Heavy Haulage, Stafford; thence United Heavy Transport and Econofreight United Heavy Haulage; now preserved by Graham Booth, Southport. Named - Musketeer
AHB807T	632	Scammell Amazon 6wl 100ton articulated tractor unit	1979	Transferred in 1982 to Wynns Heavy Haulage, Stafford
AAX543T	634	Ford Transit van	1979	Transferred in 1982 to Wynns Heavy Haulage, Stafford
AUH65T	635	Foden Fleetmaster articulated tractor unit	1979	Transferred in 1982 to Wynns Heavy Haulage, Stafford
BBO154T	637	Leyland Sherpa crewbus	1979	Transferred in 1982 to Wynns Heavy Haulage, Stafford
CAX59V	638	Leyland Sherpa crewbus	1979	Transferred in 1982 to Wynns Heavy Haulage, Stafford
BDW318V	639	Ford Transit pickup	1979	Transferred in 1982 to Wynns Heavy Haulage, Stafford
DBO661V	640	Scammell Contractor 250ton drawbar tractor	1980	Mk 2 model Contractor as RWO73R (1977); transferred in 1982 to Wynns Heavy Haulage,Stafford Named - Invincible
DBO977V	641	Ford Transit pickup	1980	Transferred in 1982 to Wynns Heavy Haulage, Stafford
FBO993V	636	Scammell Amazon 6wl 100ton articulated tractor unit	1980	Transferred in 1982 to Wynns Heavy Haulage, Stafford
EDW785V	642	Scammell Crusader articulated tractor unit	1980	Transferred in 1982 to Wynns Heavy Haulage, Stafford
ENY289V	643	Scammell Crusader articulated tractor unit	1980	Transferred in 1982 to Wynns Heavy Haulage, Stafford
ENY290V	644	Scammell Crusader articulated tractor unit	1980	Transferred in 1982 to Wynns Heavy Haulage, Stafford
GTX541W	645	Ford Transit pickup	1981	Transferred in 1982 to Wynns Heavy Haulage, Stafford
GTX542W	646	Ford Transit pickup	1981	Transferred in 1982 to Wynns Heavy Haulage, Stafford.

(Opposite Top): Nearly forgot - The Unipower Forrester Timber Tractor FDW910(189), of Feburary 1950, moving jobs, drawing two trailers, the first carrying a caterpillar tractor, the second being a steel tyred living van. A favourite photograph of the author.

Below: With a 191 ton Ferranti transformer carried on trailer 999 the outfit arrives at Rowdown Sub Station near Addington, on June 6, 1976. Leading vehicle is GTX211N (195) with JDW247F (183) at the rear

(Overleaf):A striking view by Robert Price of the 1975 Scammell Contractor 240ton drawbar tractor GTX211N (195) shown at Croydon after a year in service. Yes - they did work in the dark.

Below: Scammell Contractor RWO73R (602) on the motorway with a transformer. The rebuilt Pacific NDW345G (192) follows freerunning, ready to assist when required.

Above: Graham Booth's two preserved former Wynns Contractors' YWO24T - Musketeer and KAX395P -
                Renown, photographed at Southport in 2001.

Top left: Shown owned by Wynns Heavy Haulage, Scammell Contractor 240ton drawbar tractorYAX165T
                (631) is seen taking up the rear on a job. Delivered new to Robert Wynn & Sons Ltd in 1979 the
                vehicle was transferred to Wrekin Roadways of Telford the following year and went to the new
                Stafford based company in 1982. Three paint jobs in three years, and two more to come.

Bottom left: Normally operated as an articulated tractor unit, this rare view of Scammell Contractor KAX395P
                (600) shows the vehicle as a drawbar tractor

Overleaf: The Scammell Contractor drawbar tractor RWO73R (602) as owned by Wynns Heavy Haulage,
                Stafford.

During 1982 with the fall in the heavy haulage market brought about by the contraction of industry in the United Kingdom it was decided to amalgamate Robert Wynn & Sons Ltd with another member of United Transport - Wrekin Roadways of Telford, Shropshire, to form a new company known as Wynns Heavy Haulage with a new depot at Stafford, conveniently situated to serve the needs of their major customer, GEC. WYNNS had already disposed of their hitherto core activities some years earlier including the tipper business, crane hire, timber extraction, and had transferred their tanker fleet to another group company based at Avonmouth. They had been concentrating on the really heavy end of the market for some time and had withdrawn from the lighter low-loader business. With this development only the bigger units of the fleet together with the vehicles to service it were left, and it was these that were transferred to the new premises. This marked the closure of the depots at Newport, Chasetown and Wrekin's at Telford. After a short time the new firm was amalgamated with the other heavy haulage company within the group - Sunter Brothers of Northallerton to form another new company United Heavy Transport. Again this only lasted for a short period as a further amalgamation took place with Econofreight, the heavy haulage arm of the Transport Development Group, and thus Econofreight United Heavy Haulage was born.

The vehicles thereafter were repainted in the familiar blue and white livery of Econofreight. The Mk 2 Scammell Contractor 250ton drawbar tractor RWO73R (602) is shown operating with the new company.   (above) standing at Newport Docks in June, 1996, looking remarkably well considering that almost twenty years had elapsed since her entry into service.

(top right): hauling a heavy transformer for GEC, and
(bottom right): standing between jobs.

The vehicle is now owned by that well known Scammell enthusiast Robert Willson of Pontypool, and by coincidence is garaged within 400 yards of where I was born.

The Wynn's Preservation, Vintage and Enthusiasts Group was founded in 1987 and comprises of former employees of Robert Wynn & Sons Ltd together with friends and enthusiasts who are interested in all things to do with the old firm. It has regular meetings, social get-togethers and outings and produces a newsletter. Having disappeared over twenty ago it enables those interested in the company to keep in touch and look out for each other. Great interest is shown in preservation projects and there is a lively exchange of historical information and news.

Membership is open to anyone dedicated to keeping the WYNNS name alive and those interested in all things to do with it.

All in a days work for a WYNN'S man.

Chairman:	Roger Colcombe
Secretary:	Howard Francis (01981-240268)
Treasurer:	Mike Lucas (01633-675242
Committee:	Peter Collier
	Alan Williams
	Steve Roberts
	Brian Griffiths
	J. Hewlett
	D. Boswell
	Elwyn Edwards
	Bill Tyler
Correspondence to the secretary:	Holly Tree Cottage, Ewyas Harold, Pontrilas Herefordshire HR2 0ER

EVERYDAY FAVOURITES

THE BEST OF SINGAPORE'S RECIPES
MRS LEONG YEE SOO

Marshall Cavendish
Cuisine

EVERYDAY FAVOURITES THE BEST OF SINGAPORE'S RECIPES

All the recipes in this book are selected from the late Mrs Leong Yee Soo's original cookbooks, Singaporean Cooking, Singaporean Cooking Vol 2, Celebration Cooking and The Best of Singapore Cooking.

In Singaporean Cooking and The Best of Singapore Cooking, Mrs Rosa Lee, Mrs Dorothy Norris, Miss Marie Choo, Miss Patricia Lim, Mrs Dinah Sharif, Miss Iris Kng, Miss Chau Mei Po, Mrs Irene Oei and Miss Monica Funk were acknowledged for their help in making those books possible.

For this book, the Publisher wishes to thank **Mdm Hatijah Mohd Hassan** for the loan of her cooking and baking equipment.

Editor	:	Sim Ee Waun
Designer	:	Benson Tan
Photographer	:	Edmond Ho

First published April 2004, reprinted July 2004, September 2004, September 2005

Copyright © 2005 Marshall Cavendish International (Asia) Private Limited

Published by Marshall Cavendish Cuisine
An imprint of Marshall Cavendish International
1 New Industrial Road, Singapore 536196

Other Marshall Cavendish Offices:

Marshall Cavendish Ltd. 119 Wardour Street, London W1F OUW, UK • Marshall Cavendish Corporation. 99 White Plains Road, Tarrytown NY 10591-9001, USA • Marshall Cavendish International (Thailand) Co Ltd. 253 Asoke, 12th Flr, Sukhumvit 21 Road, Klongtoey Nua, Wattana, Bangkok 10110, Thailand • Marshall Cavendish (Malaysia) Sdn Bhd, Times Subang, Lot 46, Subang Hi-Tech Industrial Park, Batu Tiga, 40000 Shah Alam, Selangor Darul Ehsan, Malaysia

Marshall Cavendish is a trademark of Times Publishing Limited

National Library Board Singapore Cataloguing in Publication Data

Leong, Yee Soo.
Everyday favourites / Leong Yee Soo. – Singapore : Marshall Cavendish Cuisine, 2005.
p. cm. – (The best of Singapore's recipes)
Includes index.
Previously published: Times Editions, c2004.
ISBN : 981-232-649-9

1. Cookery, Singapore. I. Title. II. Series: The best of Singapore's recipes

TX724.5.S55
641.595957 -- dc21   SLS2005042798

Printed in Singapore by Times Graphics Pte Ltd

CONTENTS ●● ● ● ● ●

CONTENTS

PREFACE

MY GRANDMOTHER loved to cook and she loved to cook for the family. I remember as a child licking the cake mix from the bowl and waiting anxiously for the cake to come out of the oven. Our family had the benefit of her wonderful cooking and instructions on food preparation and methodology first hand. As in the past, my grandmother would always refer to her cookbooks while cooking, and today, many of our family members still continue with the same practice.

She spent more than 20 years perfecting her skills, constantly trying to improve her skills by experimenting with new kitchen equipment, technology and recipes. She had created her own recipes to be an easy and reliable guide so that even busy working adults could prepare delicious home cooked food. Her cookbooks were very much written to serve the needs of busy families and preserve the tradition of family cooking, especially with the increasingly hectic lifestyle of Singaporeans.

In this book, the recipes have now been reproduced with a new arrangement and photographs. It continues in the same tradition of the earlier books and pays attention to the careful preparation of dishes and a good choice of ingredients. In addition, all the useful cooking tips are still included.

We hope this book gives you a chance to experience good home cooking and good memories together with family and friends, cooking and eating together.

This book is dedicated to our grandmother's memory as a great cook, a progressive woman in her field, beloved mother, grandmother and great grandmother.

LEONG PAT LYNN & LEONG SUE LYNN

CANDLENUTS

If unavailable, use almonds, cashew nuts, Brazil nuts or macadamia nuts.

COCONUT

The milk from the coconut you use plays a very important part in the type of food or cakes that you are preparing. Be very careful and selective when choosing a coconut.

Coconuts do not come in one standard size, age and richness.

- The skinned, grated coconut referred to throughout the book is coconut which has the brown skin removed. This is to give the milk an extra whiteness. It also gives a rich natural colour to the food.
- When buying a coconut, bear in mind the type of food or cake you are preparing. For most types of food that require coconut milk, choose a freshly cut coconut with a dark brown skin as this gives rich and sweet milk. For cakes, you need to see to the requirements of your recipe. For example, if the recipe calls for 'coarsely grated coconut', then you should choose one that has a light brown skin; it is younger than the dark brown and is tender and not stringy. For special recipes like 'Sar-Sargon', you require coconut that is tender and young, ie. the skin of the coconut must be pale in colour.
- For cakes that need coarsely grated coconut to be sprinkled over, it is safer to rub a little fine salt lightly over the coconut. Place it in a shallow baking tin and steam over rapidly boiling water for 3 minutes. Cool completely before use. This will keep the coconut from turning sour.
- For every 455 g (1 lb) of grated coconut, you should be able to extract about 225–255 ml (1–1^1/$_8$ cups) milk when the coconut is fresh. Therefore, make sure the coconut is freshly cut for the day and not one that has been cut and kept overnight. See that the coconut is free of mildew or has not turned yellow in some parts

- One interesting point to note is that the amount of milk you get from a kilogramme of grated coconut depends on the machine that grates the coconut. The rollers used in the grating machines at coconut stalls come in different degrees of fineness. As such, a machine using fine tooth rollers gives you more milk than one with coarse tooth rollers.
- To squeeze coconut for No.1 milk: take a piece of white muslin 30-cm (12-in) square, put in a small fistful, or about 55 g (2 oz), of coconut and squeeze and twist at the same time. For No.2 milk, add the amount of water required and squeeze hard.

Freezing Coconut Milk

- Buy 1.4–1.8 kg (3–4 lb) of grated coconut, squeeze for No.1 milk and set aside. Add 170 ml (^{3}/$_4$ cup) water to each 455 g (1 lb) of coconut and squeeze for No.2 milk. Collect separately. Pour the No.1 and No.2 milk in separate ice-cube trays. When frozen, remove from ice-tray and pack into plastic bags and store in the freezer. It is very useful to have a stock of frozen coconut milk always in case you need it at any time of the day. It can be used to make curries and all types of cakes.
- To use frozen coconut milk, chop the amount required. Place a little water in a saucepan and bring to a boil. Place the frozen coconut milk in a small enamel basin, place basin over the water and allow the frozen coconut to thaw, stirring occasionally. Remove coconut milk to cool as soon as it turns liquid.

KITCHEN WISDOM & TIPS ON TECHNIQUES

Making Coconut Oil for Nyonya Cakes

In a saucepan, combine 115 g (4 oz) grated coconut, 225 ml (1 cup) corn oil and 8 screwpine (pandan) leaves that have been cut into pieces. Bring to a boil and cook until coconut turns dark brown. Pour oil through a metal sieve and cool before use. Store in refrigerator to preserve freshness and for future use.

COOKING MEAT

Pork chops should be cooked over moderate heat in a very hot pan or grilled under a hot grill. This will seal in the meat juices. Brown on both sides, turning over twice; then turn it down to medium heat and cook until done, about 15–20 minutes.

For bacon, cut off the rind and snip the fat in two or three places to prevent bacon from curling during frying.

Fillet steak is the best and most tender of meat cuts; next comes sirloin, scotch, porterhouse, rump and minute steak. Marinating a steak before cooking not only gives it a better flavour but also helps to make it tender. Minute steak, however, is best grilled or fried without marinating.

COOKING OIL AND FATS

To get the best results, particularly when cooking Chinese dishes, use an equal portion of both lard and cooking oil. It gives the dish a special fragrance. In recipes that specifies that lard is preferable to cooking oil, use lard in order to get its distinct flavour.

For deep-frying, always use either refined deodorised coconut oil, palm cooking oil or corn oil. Do not use olive oil.

COOKING VEGETABLES

To fry leafy vegetables, separate the leaves from the stalk. The stalks should be placed in the pan together with any other ingredients and cooked first. Stir-fry for a minute or so before adding the leaves.

To boil and blanch vegetables, bring a saucepan of water to the boil over very high heat. When the water is boiling, add some salt, sugar and a tablespoonful of cooking oil. Add the stalks, cook for $1/2$ minute and then add the leaves. Cook for another $1/2$ minute. Use a wire ladle to remove the vegetables and drain in a colander. Rinse under a running tap and drain well before use.

Vegetables like long beans and cabbage should be cooked for 5–7 minutes only, to retain their sweetness and crispness.

When boiling bean sprouts, it is important to place them in boiling water for 1 minute. Do not add any cooking oil. Remove and drain with a wire ladle. Transfer to a basin of cold water and soak for 10 minutes or until cold. Spread thinly in a colander until ready for use. The bean sprouts will then keep without 'souring'.

FRYING

1. Before frying, ensure that the the pan is very hot before you pour in the cooking oil. To get the best results when frying vegetables:
   - Use an iron wok (kuali) as it can take and retain extreme heat, which is most important.
   - Add the cooking oil to a smoking hot wok. This prevents food from sticking to the bottom. But do not allow the oil to become smoking hot as overheated fat or oil turns bitter and loses its fine flavour.
2. For deep-frying, the cooking oil must be smoky, that is, when a faint haze of smoke rises from the oil. It is then ready for frying.
   - When deep-frying in large quantities, put enough food in the pan and keep the oil boiling all the time.

- Make sure the fat is heated until smoking hot each time you put in food to be fried.
- When frying large pieces of meat or a whole chicken, the heat must be very high for the first 5 minutes to seal in the juices. After that, lower the heat for the rest of the cooking time. This gives the meat or chicken a nice golden colour and allows it to be cooked right through.

3. After frying food that is coated with flour or breadcrumbs (this also seals in the meat juices), filter the oil through a wire sieve lined thinly with cotton wool. The oil will come out clean and free from sediments.
   - Add more fresh oil to the strained oil for future use.
4. Cooking oil that has been used to deep-fry fish and prawns should be kept separate for future use and kept for cooking fish and prawns only.
5. You may clarify hot oil by squeezing some lemon juice into it, but remember to turn off the heat first. Strain and store for future use.
6. Butter will not take intense heat when frying, so put in some cooking oil before the butter.
7. Dust food with seasoned flour before coating with or dipping in batter for frying.

KAFFIR LIME LEAVES
Locally called daun limau purut, it has waxy dark green, double leaves with a distinct fragrance. To slice finely, roll it up tightly and slice thinly parallel to the central vein. Discard the central vein which will come out in one complete strip after slicing.

LARD
The oil extracted from pork fat after it has been fried is called lard. Dice the pork fat before frying. Do not overcook or burn the fat, otherwise the oil extracted will be dark and bitter. Unlike butter or margarine, lard can take intense heat without burning so it is most suitable for food that has to be cooked over high heat.

LEMON GRASS
Lemon grass gives a pleasant fragrance to cooked dishes. Use lemon rind as a substitute only when this is not available. The fragrance comes from the bottom 7 cm (3 in) of the stalk nearest the root end. The green outer layer is removed before use. To bruise or crush lemon grass, bash with the flat surface of a cleaver or chopper.

LIME PASTE
The lime paste mentioned in some of the recipes refers to the white chalky edible lime that is used for betelnut chewing. It can be bought at any Indian grocer.

Chillies retain their crispness in certain recipes when they are soaked in lime water.

SEASONING
The salt used in many of these recipes is local fine salt and not the fine table salt. Fine table salt is used mostly in Western cakes where it can be sifted together with the flour. As table salt is finer, it is more salty than the local fine salt. So measure less salt if you use fine table salt.

Use your discretion when seasoning with salt, sugar, chilli or tamarind pulp (asam). Season to your own taste as there is no hard and fast rule for seasoning food. However, one must be precise and follow the recipe to get the best results.

MSG in recipes refers to monosodium glutamate. As a substitute, chicken stock may be used. Use 1 chicken cube for 1 tsp MSG.

KITCHEN WISDOM & TIPS ON TECHNIQUES

SCREWPINE LEAVES

Commonly called pandan leaves, this local plant is a rich, emerald green and has long, smooth pointed leaves. It imparts a special fragrance and is used widely in Asian desserts and kuih. There is no substitute. Before tying it into a knot, tear each leaf lengthwise to release the fragrance.

SELECTING MEAT, POULTRY AND SEAFOOD

Pork

Should be pink, the fat very white and the skin thin.

Beef

Choose meat that is light red and the cross-grain smooth and fine. The same applies to mutton. Do not buy dark coloured meat with fat that is yellow.

Chicken

Fresh local chickens have a much better taste and flavour than frozen ones. Frozen chicken is more suitable for roasting, frying or grilling. When buying local chicken, select one with white, smooth skin. The tip of the breastbone should be soft and pliable when pressed with the thumb. When selecting chicken for steaming, choose one that is young and tender and weighs about 1 kg (approximately 2^1/$_2$ lb). For Hainanese chicken rice, choose one that is plump at the breasts and thighs and weighs 1.6–1.8 kg (approximately 3^1/$_2$–4 lb). For grilled chicken or roast spring chicken, choose a 680–795 g (1^1/$_2$–1^3/$_4$ lb) chicken. A 1.5 kg (3–3^1/$_2$ lb) chicken is best for curries and other spicy dishes.

Duck

Select as for chicken. The smaller ones are mostly used for soups and the larger ducks for roasting or braising.

Fish

When buying fish, first of all make sure that the flesh is firm to the touch. The eyes should be shiny, the gills blood-red and the scales silvery white. Squeezing lemon juice over fish will whiten it and keep it firm when boiling or steaming.

Mix tamarind, salt and some sugar to marinate fish for ^{1}/$_2$ hour before cooking curries or tamarind dishes.

Prawns

Fresh prawns have shiny shells and are firm to the touch. The head is firmly attached to the body. Avoid buying prawns with heads loosely hanging on.

Cuttlefish

When cuttlefish is very fresh, the body is well rounded, firm and shiny. The head is stuck fast to the body and the ink pouch in the stomach is firmly attached.

SUBSTITUTE INGREDIENTS

- The purplish variety of onion is a good substitute for shallots.
- If fresh ginger, lemon grass and galangal are not easily available, use the powdered forms.
- It is always advisable to use powdered turmeric.
- Almonds, cashew nuts, Brazil nuts or macadamia nuts can be used if candlenuts are not available.

THICKENING

For Chinese dishes, thickening means to thicken the gravy so as to coat the food rather than have the gravy running over the serving plate. Cornflour is a common thickening agent and refers to tapioca flour sold in the local markets. It is also known as sago flour (refined quality, and not the type used to starch clothes).

ALUMINIUM FRYING PANS

Suitable for deep-frying as they retain a steady heat and give food a nice golden brown colour. Frying chilli paste in an aluminium pan will give the mixture a natural bright colour whereas an iron wok (kuali) will result in a darker paste, possibly with a slight taste of iron.

ALUMINIUM SAUCEPAN

The heavy flat-bottomed pan is the best buy. It is suitable for the electric or gas stove. Food is cooked easily without burning. A thin saucepan will buckle when it is overheated and will not be in contact with the electric hot plate.

CHINA CLAYPOT

Chicken and pork are usually braised and stewed in the China claypot. It simmers food very nicely without burning and has a lower rate of evaporation than other saucepans. It also retains the special flavour of foods and is widely used in Chinese homes. It is also used to cook rice and porridge. Buy one with a smooth, glazed finish.

COPPER PANS

Copper pans are rarely used for Asian recipes. A copper pan has its own rare qualities. Salted mustard has a very bright green colour when boiled in a copper pan. Copper pans are very rarely used, however, as they are very expensive.

ENAMEL SAUCEPAN

Enamel saucepans are more suitable for soups and certain types of food that contain acid like tamarind or vinegar. Chipped enamelware is vulnerable to rust.

IRON WOK

Most Chinese prefer the iron wok (kuali) to the aluminium one chiefly because the iron wok can retain extreme heat before the other ingredients are added. In an iron wok, food cooks in a shorter period of time and retain its flavour and crispness. The most important point to remember is that fried food and pounded ingredients will not stick to the bottom of the wok when it is well heated.

To season an iron wok

Place some grated coconut and water to fill up three-quarters of the wok, and boil until dry. Stir occasionally until the coconut turns black, approximately 3–4 hours.

Daily care: Do not use any detergent. Wipe wok well after each wash. If it is to be stored for a long period, grease wok lightly to prevent rust.

NON-STICK PANS

There are many brands of non-stick pans to select from. Choose carefully. Whenever possible, buy the best quality products as they work out to be the most cost effective in the long run.

Some points to remember when using non-stick pans

- Non-stick pans are ideal for frying fish and soft bean curd. In a non-stick pan, food that is to be braised or simmered require less liquid. Food does not burn easily in a non-stick pan nor does the gravy evaporate as quickly as in an ordinary pan.
- The Teflon in a non-stick pan should not be heated through. If this happens, the pan may lose its non-stick qualities. Since stir-frying requires high heat, do not stir-fry in a non-stick pan. It is always best to stir-fry in an iron wok.
- Do not use the non-stick pan as a steamer as it will again damage the Teflon.
- Never use a metal slice on a non-stick pan.
- Always pour in the cooking oil or gravy first before putting on the heat.

KITCHEN EQUIPMENT

PESTLE AND MORTAR
Insist on local granite which is white with black/grey spots. To season the pounder, grind a small handful of fine sea sand in the mortar until both the pestle and mortar are reasonably smooth.

STAINLESS STEEL PANS
Stainless steel pans look attractive and are easily cleaned, but do not heat evenly. Food burns easily, too.

SUPPLEMENTARY RECIPES

Crisp-fried Shallots
Many recipes call for crisp-fried shallots to be used as a flavourful garnish.

- Peel and slice shallots thinly and dip in salt water for a while. Rinse and drain well.
- Scatter sliced shallots on absorbent paper to dry or roll up in a tea towel for $1/2$ hour. Heat enough cooking oil for deep-frying until smoking hot. Add the sliced shallots and stir-fry over high heat until shallots turn light brown.
- Reduce the heat and continue stirring until the shallots are light golden brown. Remove at once with a wire sieve to drain. Scatter on absorbent paper to cool.
- Store in a clean, dry bottle immediately. The shallots keep crisp for months in an airtight bottle.

Fried Pounded Garlic

- Peel and pound garlic or use blender to mince the garlic.
- Place garlic in a wire sieve and immerse in salt water. Drain. Use a thin piece of muslin to further squeeze out the water.
- In a heated wok, add enough cooking oil for deep-frying. When the oil is smoking hot, put the garlic and stir-fry until it turns light brown. Reduce the heat to very low and continue stirring until garlic becomes a light golden brown.
- Remove at once with a wire sieve and scatter on absorbent paper. Cool and store as for crispy shallots.

Note:
The crispy shallots and garlic do not retain much oil when the heat is turned up just before removing from wok.

Rice

- Wash rice until water runs clear.
- Use 55 ml ($^1/_4$ cup) of water for every 30 g (1 oz) of rice.
- For 455 g (16 oz) of rice, use between 800–910 ml ($3^1/_2$–4 cups) water, depending on the quality of the rice.
- Boil the rice until the water evaporates, leaving steam holes when dry. Reduce heat to low and cook for a further $^1/_2$ hour. About 455 g (1 lb) of rice is sufficient for 8 servings.

Dried Chilli Paste

Dried chillies	225 g (8 oz), stems removed
Water	450 ml (2 cups)

- Place chillies in a saucepan three-quarter filled with cold water.
- Bring to a boil and cook for 5 minutes. Cover pan and leave chillies to soak for 10 minutes. Drain.
- Place chillies in a large basin and wash until water runs clear. Drain.
- Using an electric blender, blend half of the chillies with 225 ml (1 cup) water until very fine. Remove paste and repeat process with the other half of the chillies and water.
- Store chilli paste in a plastic container. Keep in freezer until needed.

Note:
Keep chilli paste rotating while blending. Add a little water if paste is stuck.

This recipe makes about 32 Tbsp of chilli paste.

Wet Rice or Glutinous Rice Flour

Fine rice or glutinous rice flour	625g (1 lb 6 oz)
Cold water	425 ml ($1^3/_4$ cups and 2 Tbsp)

- Place flour in a mixing bowl and gradually pour in the cold water. Stir until it becomes a firm paste.
- Use the amount required for each recipe and keep the remainder in the freezer for future use.

Note:
- The paste will keep in the freezer for 1–2 months if stored in plastic bags flattened to 2.5 cm (1 inch) thick slabs.
- Recommended brands: Superior Quality Thai Rice and Glutinous Rice Flour (Erawan Brand); Fine Rice Flour (Seagull trademark); freshly ground wet rice or glutinous rice flour are available at local wet markets.

Alkaline Water

White alkaline crystal	625 g (1 lb 6 oz)
Hot water	680 ml (3 cups)

- Place alkaline crystal in a porcelain jar or bowl. Add the hot water and stir with a wooden spoon to dissolve the crystals. Let it stand overnight.
- Strain alkaline water through a fine muslin. Store the alkaline water in a bottle for future use.

Note:
- Prepared alkaline water can be kept for almost a year. Store in a bottle.
- Alkaline water is now available at specialty bakery suppliers such as Phoon Huat.

savourybites

EVERYDAY FAVOURITES – THE BEST OF SINGAPORE'S RECIPES

Satay

BARBECUED BEEF WITH PEANUT SAUCE

Barbecued Beef

INGREDIENTS

Coriander seeds	2 Tbsp
Cumin seeds	2 tsp
Beef	455 g (1 lb), chilled and sliced

Rempah

Shallots	10, peeled
Garlic	2 cloves, peeled
Turmeric	5 g, peeled, or 1/2 tsp turmeric powder
Lemon grass	4 stalks, sliced
Galangal	2 slices, peeled

Seasoning

Dark soy sauce	1 tsp
Salt	1 tsp
Sugar	4–5 Tbsp
Cooking oil	4 Tbsp

METHOD

- Place coriander and cumin seeds in a pan and fry over low heat for 5 minutes until fragrant. Pound to a fine powder while still hot. Set aside.
- Combine *rempah* ingredients and pound to a smooth paste.
- In a bowl, combine seasoning ingredients and add to *rempah* paste. Mix well.
- Rub *rempah* paste all over the beef, then sprinkle the meat with the coriander-cumin powder. Leave to marinate for 1 hour.
- Thread seasoned meat onto bamboo sticks or fine metal skewers.
- Grill over charcoal fire or under a hot grill. Baste with a mixture of cooking oil and water to keep beef moist.

Peanut Sauce

INGREDIENTS

Peanuts	455 g (1 lb), freshly roasted and ground
Water	900 ml (4 cups)
Cooking oil	225 ml (1 cup)
Salt	2 Tbsp
Sugar	8–10 Tbsp
Lime juice	4 Tbsp, or 4 Tbsp thick tamarind water

Rempah

Shallots	15, peeled
Garlic	8 cloves, peeled
Lemon grass	2 stalks, thinly sliced, or 1 tsp grated lemon rind
Dried chillies	20–30, seeded, or 4–5 Tbsp dried chilli paste (*recipe on page 13*)
Galangal	4 thin slices, peeled

Garnish

Cucumbers	2, cut into wedges
Onions	2, peeled and cut into wedges

METHOD

- Pound *rempah* ingredients into a fine paste.
- Place peanuts and water in a saucepan and bring to a boil over low heat. Simmer until mixture becomes thick. Stir constantly for about 1/2 hour. Set aside.
- Heat cooking oil in a wok and fry pounded *rempah* until fragrant and oil separates.
- Add paste to the peanuts, then add salt, sugar and lime juice.
- Boil sauce over a low heat for 5–7 minutes until sugar is dissolved. Stir often.
- Transfer to a bowl and leave to cool.
- Serve separately with barbecued beef and garnish.

Poh Pia

FRESH SPRING ROLLS

INGREDIENTS

Poh pia skin (ready-to-use)	625 g (1 lb 6 oz)
Bamboo Shoot Filling	(*Recipe on page 20*)

Topping

Cucumber	900 g (2 lb), skinned, seeded and finely shredded
Bean sprouts	900 g (2 lb), picked, washed and scalded
Chinese parsley (coriander leaves)	8 sprigs, washed and drained
Local lettuce	455 g (1 lb), washed and drained
Crab meat	225 g (8 oz), steamed
Prawns	455 g (1 lb), shelled and deveined, fried and sliced lengthwise
Eggs	8, lightly beaten, fried into an omelette and thinly sliced
Chinese sausages	4, fried and thinly sliced
Sweet black sauce (*kicap pekat manis*)	280 ml (1¼ cups)
Garlic	30 cloves, peeled and pounded to a fine paste
Garlic	30 cloves, peeled and pounded and fried until crisp
Red chillies	455 g (1 lb), pounded to a fine paste

METHOD

To serve *poh pia*

- Place cucumber, bean sprouts, Chinese parsley, lettuce, crab meat, prawns, egg omelette and sausages on separate serving plates.
- Place the sweet black sauce, garlic paste, fried garlic and chilli paste in separate bowls.
- Arrange the *poh pia* skins on separate plates.
- Place the bamboo shoot filling in a large deep bowl.

To assemble *poh pia*

- Place a skin on a plate and spread the topping in this order: a little sweet black sauce, garlic paste and chilli paste.
- Add a piece of lettuce, some bean sprouts, shredded cucumber and a heaped spoonful of filling.
- Top with some Chinese sausages, egg omelette, prawns and crab meat. Sprinkle over with some Chinese parsley and crispy garlic and fold into a neat roll.
- Cut and serve.

Note:
Keep *Poh Pia* skin covered with a damp cloth until ready to use. As a variation, you can also make your own egg skin (*recipe on page 20*).

Bamboo Shoot Filling

INGREDIENTS

Streaky pork	900 g (2 lb)
Salt	A pinch
Prawns	455 g (1 lb), small
Cooking oil	225 ml (1 cup)
Garlic	8 Tbsp (about 30 cloves), peeled and pounded
Yellow bean paste (*taucheo*)	8 Tbsp, pounded
Salt	1–1$\frac{1}{2}$ Tbsp
Sugar	8 Tbsp
MSG	2 tsp, optional
Jicama (*bangkuang* or yam bean)	1.8 kg (4 lb), peeled and shredded
Bamboo shoots	800 g (4 lb), boiled tender and shredded
Firm bean curd (*taukwa*)	12 pieces, cut into thin strips and fried

METHOD

To cook filling

- In a saucepan, combine pork, a pinch of salt and 1 litre (4$\frac{1}{2}$ cups) water and bring to the boil for 45 minutes. Remove pork and slice into fine strips. Set aside 455 ml (2 cups) of the stock.
- Shell and devein prawns. Pound prawn shells and add 1 litre (4$\frac{1}{2}$ cups) water. Strain and set aside the stock.
- Heat cooking oil in a wok and fry pounded garlic until light brown. Add yellow bean paste, salt, sugar and MSG, if using. Stir-fry for 1 minute. Pour in the prawn stock and bring to a boil.
- Add jicama to cook, then add bamboo shoots and the 455 ml (2 cups) pork stock. Boil for $\frac{1}{2}$ hour over moderate heat.
- Lower heat, add fried bean curd strips and sliced pork. Cook for 1$\frac{1}{2}$ hours, stirring occasionally.
- Add the prawns and cook for a further 10 minutes.
- Transfer filling to a saucepan. Simmer until ready to serve.

Egg Poh Pia Skin

INGREDIENTS

Plain flour	285 g (10 oz)
Cornflour	3 Tbsp
Salt	A pinch
Eggs	10
Water	680–740 ml (3–3$\frac{1}{4}$ cups)
Cooking oil	85 ml ($\frac{1}{3}$ cup)

METHOD

- Combine plain flour, cornflour, salt and sieve into a mixing bowl.
- In another bowl, beat eggs lightly, then add water and cooking oil.
- Add egg mixture to the flour and mix to form a batter.
- Grease a well-heated omelette pan. Pour enough batter to form a thin layer over the base of the pan, like a pancake. Cook until the edges curl slightly.
- Transfer the skin onto a plate. Repeat process until all the batter is used up.

Fried Radish Cake

Radish Cake

INGREDIENTS

Chinese radish (*lo bak*)	625 g (1 lb 6 oz), skinned and finely grated
Water	900 ml (4 cups)
Salt	1 Tbsp
Sugar	4 Tbsp
MSG	1 tsp, optional
Wet rice flour	625 g (1 lb 6 oz) (*recipe on page 13*)
Non-glutinous plain flour	310 g (11 oz)
Water	900 ml (4 cups)
Cooking oil	2 Tbsp

METHOD

To prepare the cake

- Place grated radish in a saucepan of cold water and bring to the boil for 10 minutes. Drain and repeat boiling process. Drain and set aside.
- In a saucepan, combine the 900 ml (4 cups) water, salt, sugar and MSG, if using. Bring to a boil.
- In a large bowl, combine the wet rice flour, non-glutinous plain flour and the second 900 ml (4 cups) of water and stir until well blended. Pour the flour mixture gradually into the saucepan of boiling water, stirring constantly.
- Add the radish and cooking oil and reduce the heat to low.
- Using a wooden spoon, stir mixture until it becomes thick and pasty and is only half-cooked.
- Remove saucepan from the heat and pour the flour mixture into a square cake pan or into 3 loaf pans, 22 cm x 8 cm x 8 cm (8^1/$_2$ in x 3 in x 3 in).
- Place pans in a steamer and steam for 1^1/$_2$ hours.
- When cooked, remove pans from steamer and leave radish cakes to cool completely in the pans before frying (*see ingredients and method for frying on page 22*).

Note:
Steamed radish cake can be kept in the refrigerator for a week.

For Frying Radish Cake

INGREDIENTS

Radish cake	8 pcs, 8 cm x 8 cm x 1-cm thick (3 in x 3 in x 1/2-in)
Eggs	4
Dark soy sauce	2 Tbsp
Garlic	1 Tbsp, peeled and pounded
Chilli sauce	2–4 Tbsp (see recipe below)
Sweet black sauce (kicap pekat manis)	2 Tbsp
Salted radish (chai poh)	2 Tbsp, chopped
Spring onions	3, cut into 0.5-cm (1/4-in) lengths
Pepper	To taste
Lard for frying	

METHOD

- Halve all the ingredients. Fry in two batches.
- Heat an iron wok until smoking hot. Add some lard and fry radish cake pieces until brown and slightly crisp.
- Push radish cake pieces to one side of wok.
- Add 2 Tbsp lard into the wok and heat through. Break in eggs and spread them in a thin layer and cook.
- Stir the radish cake pieces into the eggs and mix. Add the dark soy sauce and stir-fry, chopping radish cake pieces as you go along.
- Push radish cake mixture to one side of wok again, add 1 Tbsp lard and fry garlic until light brown.
- Add 1 or 2 Tbsp chilli sauce into the wok and push the radish cake mixture back into the centre of the wok to combine. Add sweet black sauce and salted radish with another 1 or 2 Tbsp lard. Stir-fry for another 1–2 minutes. Lastly add the spring onions.
- Transfer fried radish cake to a plate, add pepper and serve.
- Repeat process with the other half of the ingredients.

Chilli Sauce

INGREDIENTS

Lard	1 Tbsp
Garlic	1 Tbsp, peeled and chopped
Shrimp paste (belacan)	3/4 tsp, crumbled
Dried chilli paste	285 ml (1/4 cup) (recipe on page 13)
Water	340 ml (1 1/2 cups)
Salt	1 1/2 Tbsp
Sugar	1 Tbsp
Pepper	1 tsp

METHOD

- Heat lard in a small saucepan. Add garlic and shrimp paste and fry until brown and fragrant.
- Add the rest of the ingredients into the pan and bring to a boil for 5 minutes over gentle heat.
- Cool and use as required.

Bak Pow

MEAT BUNS

INGREDIENTS

Filling

Pork	1.2 kg (2 lb 11 oz), thinly sliced
Chinese sausages	4, diced

Marinade for Filling

Dark soy sauce	2 Tbsp
Soy sauce	1 tsp
Oyster sauce	2 tsp
Pepper	1 tsp
Salt	$1\frac{1}{2}$ tsp
Sugar	4 heaped tsp
Sesame oil	1 tsp
Peanut butter	4 Tbsp
Cornstarch or cornflour	3 Tbsp
Lard	2 Tbsp
MSG	2 tsp, optional
Spring onions	1 tsp, coarsely chopped

The Bun

Self-raising flour	455 g (1 lb)
Baking powder	2 Tbsp
Castor sugar	85 g (3 oz)
Water	200 ml ($\frac{3}{4}$ cup plus 2 Tbsp), hot
Lard	55 g (2 oz)

METHOD

To prepare the filling

- Place pork slices and Chinese sausages in a bowl. Add the marinade ingredients and mix well. Set aside for 1 hour before filling.

To prepare the bun

- In a bowl, combine self-raising flour and baking powder. Make a well in the centre and add the sugar.
- Pour in the hot water and stir to dissolve the sugar.
- Bring in half of the flour from the sides to mix with the sugar.
- Add lard. Using your fingertips, rub in the rest of the flour with the lard until well blended.
- Leave dough to stand for 15 minutes.
- Divide the dough into 3 portions and cut each portion into 8 equal pieces.
- Roll each piece into a ball, press to flatten and place some of the filling in the centre. Bring the edges of the dough together and pleat the edges to seal.
- Put each bun on a small square piece of grease-proof paper and leave for 10 minutes in a warm place.
- Steam over rapidly boiling water for 10 minutes. (Do not lift lid while steaming).
- Serve hot.

Chwee Kway

STEAMED RICE CAKES WITH SALTED RADISH

INGREDIENTS

Water	560 ml (2^1/$_2$ cups)
Salt	^{1}/$_2$ tsp
Rice flour	140 g (5 oz)
Sago flour	1 Tbsp , heaped
Cooking oil	2 Tbsp

Topping

Pork fat	170 g (6 oz), diced, washed and drained
Garlic	2 cloves, peeled and lightly crushed
Salted radish (*chai po*)	115 g (4 oz), chopped
MSG	^{1}/$_2$ tsp, optional
Pepper	To taste

METHOD

- In a bowl, combine 225 ml (1 cup) of the water, salt, the flours and mix well. Add the cooking oil and beat with a fork until well blended. Set aside.
- In a saucepan, bring the rest of the water to a boil, then pour it gradually into the flour mixture, stirring constantly to prevent lumps forming.
- Steam the empty *chwee kway* moulds (*see picture on the left below*) over moderate heat for 5 minutes.
- Then pour the flour mixture into the moulds and steam for another 10–15 minutes or until well cooked.
- Remove the *chwee kway* from the steamer. Leave *chwee kway* in the moulds to cool – about 10 minutes.
- When cool, remove them from the moulds to serve, topped with salted radish.

To cook the topping

- In a small saucepan, combine lard and garlic and fry until lard turns light brown.
- Remove the garlic and lard and discard. Add in chopped salted radish, MSG, if using, and pepper and cook gently over low heat for ^{1}/$_2$ hour. Stir to prevent burning.
- To serve, place *chwee kway* on a plate and top with a spoonful of cooked radish. Sweet chilli sauce can be added if desired.

Note:
Keep the leftovers in the refrigerator. To serve, steam the *chwee kway* to heat through and top with preserved salted radish. You can buy ready-chopped salted radish from most supermarkets or Asian speciality shops.

Otak–Otak Panggang

SPICY FISH GRILLED IN BANANA LEAVES

INGREDIENTS

Coconut	680 g (1 1/2 lb), grated
Spanish mackerel (*ikan tenggiri*)	1.2 kg (2 lb 11 oz)
Water	170 ml (3/4 cup)
Salt	A pinch
Eggs	2, lightly beaten
Kaffir lime leaves (*daun limau purut*)	2, finely sliced
Turmeric leaves (*daun kunyit*)	4, finely sliced
Banana leaves	26, cut into 22 cm x 20 cm (10 in x 8 in) sheets, washed and scalded

Rempah

Onions	2, about 225 g (8 oz), peeled
Galangal	30 slices, about 85 g (3 oz), peeled
Candlenuts	5, crushed
Dried chillies	25, soaked to soften
Shrimp paste (*belacan*)	1 Tbsp
Turmeric	20 g, peeled

Seasoning

Sugar	3 Tbsp
Salt	2 Tbsp
MSG	1 tsp, optional
Cooking oil	3 Tbsp
Coriander seeds	2 tsp, roasted

METHOD

- Using a piece of muslin, squeeze grated coconut to extract 285 ml (1 1/4 cups) of No.1 milk. Collect in a bowl and set aside.
- Combine *rempah* ingredients and grind to a fine paste. Set aside.
- Bone and fillet the fish. Using a spoon, scrape half of the meat into a bowl. Thinly slice the remaining meat.
- Pound or mince the scraped fish meat until smooth. Add 170 ml (3/4 cup) water and a pinch of salt. Beat mixture with your hands until it forms a sticky paste.
- Add the No.1 milk and continue beating until well blended. Add the eggs, *rempah* paste and seasoning ingredients and mix thoroughly until well blended. Add the sliced fish, lime leaves and turmeric leaves and mix well.
- Place 2 Tbsp of fish mixture in the middle of each banana leaf, fold it into a long rectangular package and fasten the two ends of the leaf with a stapler or a sharp toothpick.
- Preheat grill. When very hot, place wrapped fish about 8 cm (3 in) from the hot grill, and cook for 7–10 minutes on each side.

Ngoh Hiang

MEAT ROLLS

INGREDIENTS

Dried bean curd skin	2 pieces
Eggs	2, lightly beaten
Pork	455 g (1 lb), minced
Prawns	225 g (8 oz), shelled, deveined, and coarsely chopped
Onion	1, peeled and finely chopped
Crab meat	170 g (6 oz), steamed
Cooking oil for deep-frying	
Cucumber	1/2, sliced for garnishing

Seasoning

Salt	1 tsp
Sugar	2 tsp
MSG	1 tsp, optional
Soy sauce	2 tsp
Dark soy sauce	1 tsp
Pepper	1 tsp
Lard or cooking oil	1 Tbsp
Plain flour	1 Tbsp
Five-spice powder	1 rounded tsp

METHOD

- Cut bean curd skin into rectangles 15 cm x 18 cm (6 in x 7 in). Set aside.
- Prepare the filling: In a large bowl, combine seasoning ingredients with the eggs, then add pork, prawns, onion and the crab meat. Mix well.
- Place a small portion of the filling mixture on a piece of bean curd skin and roll into a cigar shape. Seal ends with a little plain flour mixed with water.
- Steam the *ngoh hiang* for 10 minutes, then leave to cool.
- Now, deep-fry them.
- When cool, slice and serve with cucumber.

Murtabak

INGREDIENTS

Plain flour	455 g (1 lb)
Pepper	1/2 tsp
Baking powder	3/4 tsp
Salt	3/4 tsp
Water	340 ml (1 1/2 cups)
Ghee	
Filling	(See recipe below)
Eggs	4, beaten

METHOD

- Combine flour, pepper, baking powder and salt and sift together into a bowl.
- Add the water and blend to form a smooth dough. Cover bowl and leave overnight.
- Divide dough into 4 equal portions. Roll out thinly on an oiled marble or formica table top, and spread ghee liberally over the dough. Fold and shape into balls. Cover with a damp cloth. Set aside for 1/2 hour.
- Roll out each ball into a thin rectangle.
- Spread filling in the middle of the dough and lightly brush beaten egg over the meat.
- Fold dough over the filling to form a rectangle or square dumpling and fry in hot ghee until brown on both sides. Serve hot.

Filling

INGREDIENTS

Cooking oil for frying	
Minced mutton or veal	600 g (1 lb 5 oz)
Ground turmeric	1/4 tsp
MSG	1/2 tsp, optional
Salt	1/2 tsp

Spice Mix

Coriander seeds	2 heaped Tbsp, roasted
Aniseeds	2 level Tbsp
Cardamom seeds	20, husk removed

Seasoning

Onions	600 g (1 lb 5 oz), peeled and diced
Turmeric powder	1/4 tsp
Salt	1/2 tsp
MSG	1/2 tsp, optional

METHOD

- Combine spice mix ingredients and pound finely.
- Add a little cooking oil into a pan and heat. When hot, add minced meat, ground turmeric, MSG, if using, and salt and fry. When cooked, transfer to a plate and set aside.
- Now, add 2 Tbsp cooking oil into a pan and heat. When hot, add seasoning ingredients into the pan and fry for 2 minutes.
- Return the meat into the pan and add the pounded spice mix. Stir to combine and adjust seasoning.
- Transfer to a plate. When cool, use filling to prepare the *murtabak*.

Char Siew Pow

STEAMED ROAST PORK BUNS

INGREDIENTS

Filling

Plain flour	1 Tbsp
Cooking oil	2 Tbsp
Lard or cooking oil	2 Tbsp
Garlic	2 cloves, peeled and finely chopped
Onions	55 g (2 oz), peeled and finely chopped
Roast pork (*char siew*)	285 g (10 oz), diced small

Marinade for Filling

Sugar	5 tsp
Pepper	1/2 tsp
Sesame oil	1 tsp
Dark soy sauce	1 tsp
Soy sauce	1 tsp
Water	115 ml (1/2 cup)

The Bun

Self-raising flour	455 g (1 lb)
Baking powder	2 Tbsp
Castor sugar	85 g (3 oz)
Water	200 ml (3/4 cup plus 2 Tbsp), hot
Lard	55 g (2 oz)

METHOD

To prepare the filling

- In a bowl, combine marinade ingredients and set aside for later use.
- In another bowl, combine the plain flour with the 2 Tbsp of cooking oil from the filling ingredients. Mix well and set aside.
- In a pan, heat some cooking oil and fry garlic until light brown. Add chopped onions and cook until transparent. Pour in marinade and bring to the boil over medium heat.
- Add in the roast pork, stir for a moment, then add flour and oil mixture. Mix well, cook for 1/2 minute and transfer to a plate to cool.
- Chill in refrigerator before using.

To prepare the bun

- In a bowl, combine self-raising flour and baking powder. Make a well in the centre and add the sugar.
- Pour in the hot water and stir to dissolve the sugar.
- Push in half of the flour from the sides to mix with the sugar.
- Add the lard and using your fingertips, rub it into the rest of the flour until well blended. Leave dough to stand for 15 minutes.
- Divide the dough into 3 portions and cut each portion into 8 equal pieces.
- Roll each piece into a ball, press to flatten and place some of the filling in the center. Bring the edges of the dough together at the top and pleat the edges to seal.
- Put each bun on a small square piece of grease-proof paper and leave for 10 minutes in a warm place.
- Steam over rapidly boiling water for 10 minutes. (Do not lift lid while steaming).
- Serve hot.

Tauhu Goreng

FRIED BEAN CURD WITH PEANUT SAUCE

INGREDIENTS

Water	570 ml (2^1/$_2$ cups)
Firm bean curd (*taukwa*)	10 large pieces, soaked in salted water and drained
Bean sprouts	625 g (1 lb 6 oz), picked and blanched
Cucumber	625 g (1 lb 6 oz), sliced

Sauce

Garlic	3 Tbsp, peeled and pounded
Red chillies	10, pounded finely
Green chillies	8, pounded finely
Bird's eye chillies (*cili padi*)	10–20, optional, finely pounded
Dried chilli paste	1–2 Tbsp (*recipe on page 13*)
Dark soy sauce	4–6 Tbsp
Sugar	6–8 Tbsp
Palm sugar (*gula Melaka*)	4 Tbsp, flaked
Vinegar	4 Tbsp
Peanuts	625 g (1 lb 6 oz), roasted and ground

METHOD

- Prepare the sauce: In a large bowl, combine all the sauce ingredients and half the water.
- Blend to a smooth paste, the add the rest of the water. Stir well.
- Place bean curd in a pan and fry. Remove from pan and cut into pieces.
- Arrange bean curd on a plate and top with bean sprouts and cucumber.
- Pour sauce over it and serve immediately.

Note:
This recipe serves 10.

Steamed Radish Cake

INGREDIENTS

Chinese radish (*lo bak*)	625 g (1 lb 6 oz)
Water	855 ml (3³/₄ cups)
Salt	1 Tbsp
Sugar	3 Tbsp
MSG	1 Tbsp, optional
Wet rice flour	625 g (1 lb 6 oz) (*recipe on page 13*)
Non-glutinous plain flour	285 g (10 oz)
Water	800 ml (3¹/₂ cups)
Waxed pork	115 g (4 oz), diced (may be substituted with roast pork or *char siew*)
Chinese sausages	4, diced
Dried prawns	115g (4 oz), washed and drained
Lard	1 Tbsp

METHOD

- Skin and grate radish.
- Place grated radish in a saucepan of water and boil for 7 minutes.
- Drain. Pour cold water into saucepan together with the radish and boil again for another 7 minutes. Drain and set aside.
- Place the 855 ml (3³/₄ cups) water in a saucepan together with the salt, sugar and MSG, if using, and bring to the boil to make a stock.
- In a large mixing bowl, combine the two flours and the 800 ml (3¹/₂ cups) water and mix well. Add the radish.
- Slowly add the boiled stock to the radish mixture. Stir constantly.
- Heat a wok. When hot, pour in the radish mixture. Lower the heat and cook until mixture turns pasty and begins to thicken. (This is when it is half cooked.)
- At this point, add the waxed pork, Chinese sausage and dried prawns. Mix well.
- Transfer to a greased square pan (*see picture on the left*) and steam for 1–2 hours or until cake shrinks a little from the sides of tin. Leave to cool overnight.
- Cut into 1-cm (¹/₂-in) thick pieces. In a heated pan, add lard and radish and fry. Serve hot with chilli sauce on the side.

Morokoo

BLACK BEAN FLOUR AND COCONUT CRISPS

INGREDIENTS

Coconut	1.2 kg (2 lb 11 oz), skinned and grated (to extract milk)
Rice flour	445 g (1 lb)
Black bean flour	115 g (4 oz)
Oom (*ajowan*) seeds	2 tsp
Cumin seeds	4 tsp, whole
Turmeric powder	1/2 tsp
Salt	2 tsp
Coconut	55 g (2 oz), grated
Cooking oil	2 litres (8 3/4 cups) for deep-frying

METHOD

- Use the 1.2 kg (2 1/2 lbs) grated coconut to extract coconut milk. Place handfuls of the coconut in a piece of muslin and squeeze to extract No.1 milk. You should have 455 ml (2 cups) of the milk. Collect in a bowl and set aside.
- In a large mixing bowl, combine the rice flour, black bean flour, oom seeds, cumin seeds, turmeric powder, salt and the 55 g (2 oz) grated coconut. Using your hand, mix the ingredients until well combined.
- Slowly add the No.1 milk and knead to form a smooth, semi-firm dough. Allow to rest for 1/2 hour.
- Put dough in a *morokoo* press to test for texture. It should flow easily leaving a clear pattern.
- Heat cooking oil in an aluminium wok until hot. Fill *morokoo* press with the dough and press dough into the heated oil, spreading it around the wok. Fry over moderately high heat until golden brown. Do this in batches.
- Use a wire mesh ladle to remove *morokoo* from the oil. Drain on absorbent paper.
- When it is still warm, store it in an airtight container.

Note:
Morokoo continues to brown for a while after it has been removed from the pan. As such, do not allow it to brown excessively in the pan. Excessive frying will also cause *morokoo* to lose its delicate flavour. Make sure *morokoo* is crispy right through.

Black bean flour and oom seeds are available from Indian grocery stores that sell spices. It is preferable to buy the beans, fry them over low heat and mill them.

For rice flour, use locally milled rice flour or wash Thai rice, air dry and mill.

Chee Cheong Fun

INGREDIENTS

Rice flour	140 g (5 oz)
Sago flour	2 Tbsp
Water	570 ml (2$\frac{1}{2}$ cups)
Salt	$\frac{1}{2}$ tsp
Cooking oil	2 Tbsp
Crisp-fried shallots	4 Tbsp (recipe on page 12)
Sesame seeds	4 Tbsp, toasted

METHOD

- In a bowl, combine the rice and sago flours with 255 ml (1 cup) of the water. Add salt and cooking oil, mix well and set aside.
- Place the remaining 345 ml (1$\frac{1}{2}$ cups) of water in a saucepan and bring to a boil. Then slowly add it to the flour mixture, stirring as you pour.
- To steam: Grease two 23-cm (9-in) round cake pans and steam the empty pans for 2 minutes to heat through.
- Stir the flour mixture and pour a ladle, or 115–140 ml ($\frac{1}{2}$–$\frac{1}{3}$ cup) of it into the pans. Tilt pans about to spread the flour mixture evenly over the pan.
- Steam for about 1–1$\frac{1}{2}$ minutes or until the mixture turns transparent.
- Remove pans from the wok and put over a shallow basin of cold water to cool.
- Using a spatula, remove the cooked *chee cheong fun*. Form into long rolls and place on a plate.
- To serve: Cut *chee cheong fun* into 2–3-cm (1–1$\frac{1}{2}$-in) lengths. Place on a serving place, sprinkle with crisp-fried shallots and sesame seeds and serve with mushroom soy sauce (*see recipe below*) and chilli sauce. Sliced roast pork strips (*char siew*) or small steamed prawns may also be added.

Mushroom Soy Sauce

INGREDIENTS

Cooking oil	1 Tbsp
Sugar	2 Tbsp
Ginger	4 slices, peeled
Mushroom soy sauce	55 ml ($\frac{1}{4}$ cup)
Water	55 ml ($\frac{1}{4}$ cup)
MSG	1 tsp, optional

METHOD

- In a saucepan, heat cooking oil, sugar and ginger until sugar turns light brown.
- Pour in the mushroom soy sauce, water and MSG, if using. Bring to a boil for 5 minutes.
- Remove, cool and serve.

Soon Kway

INGREDIENTS

Rice flour	300 g (10½ oz)
Water	570 ml (2½ cups)
Salt	½ tsp
Pheng say	A pinch (*available at Chinese dispensaries*)
Sago flour	70 g (2½ oz)
Cooking oil	55 ml (¼ cup)

METHOD

- In a cup, combine 2 Tbsp rice flour and 170 ml (¾ cup) water. Mix well and set aside.
- In a saucepan, combine the rest of the water, salt and *pheng say* and bring to a boil. Turn down the heat, pour in the flour-and-water mixture and stir well.
- Add in the remaining rice flour and stir with a wooden spoon until the paste becomes smooth. Remove from heat.
- Transfer rice paste to a large basin or tray. Add sago flour and cooking oil and knead for 5 minutes.
- Divide dough into egg-sized portions and roll each portion into a flat oval. Place 2 Tbsp of the filling (*see recipe below*) in the middle of the oval, and fold dough in half over the filling to form a semi-circular dumpling.
- To seal, pinch the edges together to resemble a curry puff.
- Place *soon kway* on an oiled steamer tray and steam for 10–12 minutes.
- Serve hot with chilli sauce.

Filling

INGREDIENTS

Jicama (*bangkuang* or yam bean)	455 g (1 lb)
Lard or cooking oil	3 Tbsp
Garlic	1 Tbsp , peeled and pounded
Yellow bean paste (*taucheo*)	1 Tbsp , pounded
Sugar	1 tsp
MSG	½ tsp, optional
Salt	½ tsp
Water	115 ml (½ cup)
Small dried prawns	55 g (2 oz), washed
Prawn	170 g (6 oz), optional

METHOD

- Peel and slice jicama into thin strips, immerse in water and drain.
- Heat lard or cooking oil in a pan and fry garlic until light brown. Add the yellow bean paste, sugar, MSG, if using, and salt and fry for a moment.
- Add the water, dried and fresh prawns if using and bring to a boil.
- Add the jicama, stir and cook over moderate heat until almost dry. Cool before use.

Kuih Chang Babi

GLUTINOUS RICE DUMPLING

INGREDIENTS

Rice

Glutinous rice	2 kg (4½ lb), soaked overnight
Salt	3 Tbsp
Pepper	3 tsp
Water	510 ml (2¼ cups)
Lard	420 g (15 oz)
Screwpine (*pandan*) leaves	30–35, large, about 8 cm x 55 cm (3½ in x 22 in)

Filling

Water	850 ml (3¾ cups)
Lean pork	1.2 kg (42 oz)
Pork fat	115 g (4 oz)
Lard or cooking oil	200 ml (2 cups)
Garlic	55 g (2 oz), peeled and finely pounded
Shallots	225 g (8 oz), peeled and finely pounded
Salt	1 rounded tsp
Sugar	395 g (14 oz)
Pepper	3 Tbsp
Dark soy sauce	4 Tbsp
Dried Chinese mushrooms	55 g (2 oz), soaked and finely diced
Sugared winter melon (*tung kwa*)	225 g (8 oz), diced
Coriander seeds	6 Tbsp, roasted and ground

METHOD

To prepare rice

- Drain glutinous rice and divide into three portions.
- Using chopsticks, make steam holes in one portion of the rice. Steam over rapidly boiling water for 20 minutes.
- Remove glutinous rice and place in a saucepan.
- Combine 1 Tbsp of the salt, 1 tsp of the pepper and 170 ml (¾ cup) of the water and pour around the steamed glutinous rice. Mix well.
- Cover for 10 minutes. Then mix 140 g (5 oz) of the lard evenly with the glutinous rice. Keep warm in a saucepan with a tight fitting lid.
- Repeat process with the other 2 portions of the glutinous rice.
- Put all the steamed glutinous rice in the saucepan and keep warm.

To prepare filling

- In a saucepan, combine 850 ml (3¾ cups) water, pork and pork fat and bring to a boil. Keep it boiling over moderately high heat for 20 minutes.
- Remove pork and fat and leave aside to cool. Dice pork and fat and set aside. Continue boiling until stock is reduced to 455 ml (2 cups).
- Add lard or cooking oil to a heated wok. When hot, add the pounded garlic and pounded shallots and fry until fragrant. Add in pork, salt, sugar, pepper and dark soy sauce and stir to combine. Continue cooking until pork changes colour.
- Add the stock, mushrooms, sugared melon and pork fat and continue cooking over medium heat for ½ hour.
- Add the ground coriander and stir. Reduce heat and simmer until meat filling is almost dry. Leave to cool and keep overnight before assembling the dumplings.

To wrap dumplings

- Take 1 broad or 2 narrow screwpine leaves, fold from the centre of the leaf to form a cone. Take a fistful of steamed glutinous rice and press firmly into the cone.
- Make a well in the centre of the glutinous rice while pressing the rice evenly to the sides of the cone.
- Put 2–3 Tbsp of the pork filling in the well. Then take some of the glutinous rice which has been flattened against the sides of the cone and cover the filling.
- Fold the leaf over to cover and tie tightly with string.
- Tie dumplings in groups of 10. Boil them in a large pot of water with 2 Tbsp salt for 3–3½ hours.

Note:
Unwrap a dumpling to see if the rice is smooth. If not, boil for 30–40 minutes more. Hang dumplings to dry for 1–2 hours after cooking to prevent sogginess.

Sugared winter melon is available in most Chinese grocery stores.

soups&salads

EVERYDAY FAVOURITES – THE BEST OF SINGAPORE'S RECIPES

Bak Kut Teh

SPICY SPARERIB CONSOMME

INGREDIENTS

Pork spareribs	625 g (1 lb 6 oz), cut into small pieces
Salt	$^1/_2$ tsp
Pepper	$^1/_2$ tsp
Lard	3 Tbsp
Sugar	1 Tbsp
Garlic	2 cloves, crushed
Yellow bean paste (*taucheo*)	1 tsp, pounded
Water	1.4 litres (6$^1/_4$ cups), hot

Seasoning

Star anise	2 petals
Cinnamon quill	2.5-cm (1-in) length
Peppercorns	1 tsp
Salt	1 tsp
MSG	1 tsp, optional
Dark soy sauce	1 tsp

Garnish

Chinese cruellers, sliced	
Crisp-fried shallots	1 Tbsp (*recipe on page 12*)

METHOD

- Marinate spareribs with salt and pepper for $^1/_2$ hour.
- Heat pan until very hot. Add 2 Tbsp lard and fry spareribs until well browned. Transfer to a dish.
- In a clean pan, heat 1 Tbsp lard. Add sugar and heat until caramelised and light brown.
- Add garlic and yellow bean paste and stir-fry for $^1/_2$ minute. Return the spareribs to the pan together with the hot water and seasoning ingredients.
- Bring it to a rapid boil for 10 minutes, then reduce the heat and simmer for 1$^1/_2$–1$^3/_4$ hours or until the meat is tender. Skim excess oil from the surface.
- To serve: Place spareribs and soup in a bowl, top with crisp-fried shallots and serve with white rice and Chinese cruellers.

Soto Ayam

INDONESIAN CHICKEN SOUP

INGREDIENTS

Chicken	1, about 1.2 kg (2 lb 11 oz), including cleaned liver and gizzard
Salt	1 tsp
Cooking oil	1 Tbsp
Salt	2–3 tsp
MSG	2 tsp, optional
Water	5 litres (22 cups)
Bird eye's chillies (*cili padi*)	1–2 Tbsp, finely pounded
Dark soy sauce	4 Tbsp
Sugar	1 tsp
Eggs	4, hard-boiled, shelled and diced
Potatoes	225 g (8 oz), boiled, peeled and diced
Cellophane noodles (*tang hoon*)	30 g (1 oz), soaked in hot water

Aromatics

Shallots	8, peeled and coarsely chopped
Garlic	2 cloves, peeled and crushed
Peppercorns	1 tsp
Turmeric	10 g (1/2 Tbsp), peeled
Candlenuts	4, lightly crushed
Ginger	20g (1 Tbsp), peeled and lightly crushed
Lemon grass	3 stalks, bruised

Garnish

Chinese celery	4 sprigs, sliced
Spring onions	2, sliced
Crisp-fried shallots	2 cups (*recipe on page 12*)
Lime (*limau nipis*)	8, cut into wedges

METHOD

- Wash the chicken and rub with 1 tsp salt. Set aside.
- Heat cooking oil in a pan, add aromatics and fry over a high heat for 2 minutes. Remove from pan and set aside.
- Place 2–3 tsp of salt, MSG, if using, and water into a pan and bring to a boil. Add the fried aromatics, chicken, liver and gizzard. Cover the pan and let simmer for 45 minutes.
- Remove the chicken, liver and gizzard and place in a basin of cold water for 10 minutes to cool.
- When cool enough to handle, debone the chicken, dice the meat and set aside.
- Return the bones to the stock. Boil gently for 1 1/2 hours. Strain the stock and leave to simmer until ready to serve.
- Combine bird's eye chillies, dark soy sauce and sugar in a bowl.
- Serve individually. Place some of the eggs, potatoes and cellophane noodles in individual soup bowls. Add soup and top with garnish ingredients. Add chilli sauce and a squeeze of lime juice to taste. Serve hot.

Sup Kambing

MUTTON SOUP

INGREDIENTS

Mutton ribs	1.8 kg (4 lbs), cut into pieces
Water	3.6 litres (16 cups)
Salt	2 Tbsp
MSG	1–2 tsp, optional
Cinnamon quill	10-cm (4-in) length
Cardamom seeds	20, crushed
Star anise	1
Bicarbonate of soda	1/2 tsp
Sheep trotters	4, cut into short lengths
Plain flour	6 Tbsp
Quick cooking oats	2 Tbsp, finely pounded
Water	225 ml (1 cup)
Crisp-fried shallots	1/2 cup (recipe on page 12)
Chinese celery	15 sprigs, washed and sliced

Marinade

Shallots	285 g (10 oz), peeled
Garlic	55 g (2 oz), peeled
Ginger	115 g (4 oz), peeled
Nutmeg	1/2 piece
Pepper	2 tsp
Turmeric powder	1 tsp
Ground cumin	1 tsp
Ground coriander	2 Tbsp

METHOD

- Prepare the marinade: Pound together shallots, garlic, ginger and nutmeg to a fine paste. Add pepper, ground turmeric, ground cumin and ground coriander and mix thoroughly.
- Rub marinade all over the ribs and leave for 1/2 hour.
- Place 3.6 litres (16 cups) water, cinnamon quill, cardamom seeds and star anise in a saucepan and bring to a boil.
- Add the marinated ribs, salt and MSG, if using.
- Boil rapidly for 20 minutes, then turn down the heat. Simmer for 1 1/2–2 hours or until ribs are tender.
- Place trotters in a small saucepan, add 455 ml (2 cups) of the soup and the bicarbonate of soda and bring to a boil. Let it simmer until the trotters are tender.
- Pour the soup and trotters back into the saucepan of ribs and bring to a boil again.
- In a bowl, combine plain flour, oats and the 225 ml (1 cup) water. Stir to blend, then gradually pour it into the soup and stir.
- Simmer until ready to serve.
- To serve: Dish the soup and meat into a large bowl or into individual soup bowls. Garnish with crisp-fried shallots and Chinese celery.

Ju Her Eng Chye

CUTTLEFISH SALAD

INGREDIENTS

Fried bean curd (*taukwa*)	6 pieces
Water convolvulus (*kangkung*)	285 g (10 oz), washed and picked
Processed cuttlefish	225 g (8 oz), thickly sliced
Processed jellyfish	55 g (2 oz), thinly sliced
Sesame seeds	2 Tbsp, toasted

Dressing

Chilli sauce	4–6 Tbsp
Hoisin sauce	3 Tbsp
Lime juice	1 Tbsp
Peanut oil	1 Tbsp
Sesame oil	1/2 tsp

METHOD

- Combine the dressing ingredients in a bowl and set aside.
- Toast fried bean curd until crispy. Cut into pieces.
- In a pot, place some water, 1 tsp each of salt and sugar and 1 Tbsp cooking oil and bring to a boil. Blanch water convolvulus for 10 seconds and remove. Drain well and transfer to a large plate.
- Arrange cuttlefish, jellyfish and bean curd on top of the vegetables, and sprinkle with toasted sesame seeds. Pour dressing onto the vegetables and serve.

Chinese Rojak

INGREDIENTS

Kalamansi lime (*limau kesturi*) juice	1 Tbsp
Tamarind pulp (*asam*)	1 Tbsp, soaked in 85 ml (¹/₃ cup) water, squeezed and strained
Peanuts	225 g (8 oz), roasted and ground
Chinese cruellers	2, thickly sliced
Fried bean curd puffs (*taupok*)	4 squares, cut into pieces
Cucumber	170 g (6 oz), sliced
Bean sprouts	115 g (4 oz), picked, blanched and drained
Jicama (*bangkuang* or yam bean)	170 g (6 oz), sliced
Pineapple	170 g (6 oz), sliced
Water convolvulus (*kangkung*)	115 g (4 oz), picked, blanched, drained and cut into 5-cm (2-in) lengths

Dressing

Sugar	7–8 Tbsp
Salt	1– 1¹/₄ tsp
Dried chilli paste	2–4 Tbsp (*recipe on page 13*)
Black prawn paste (*hay ko*)	2–2¹/₂ Tbsp

METHOD

- Combine dressing ingredients in a large bowl and blend to a paste with the back of a wooden spoon.
- Add the lime juice and 4–5 Tbsp of the tamarind water and mix well.
- Add peanuts to the remaining tamarind water and stir well. Add the vegetables and stir with a wooden spoon to combine.
- Just before serving, add the Chinese cruellers and fried bean curd puffs. Mix well.

Indian Rojak

INGREDIENTS

Potato	225 g (8 oz), boiled, skinned and quartered
Eggs	8, hard boiled, shelled and quartered
Firm bean curd (*taukwa*)	5, fried and cut into pieces
Cucumber	2, skinned and sliced
Lettuce leaves	2, shredded
Coconut fingers	(*Recipe on page 61*), thickly sliced
Warday	(*Recipe on page 61*)
Prawn fritters	(*Recipe on page 62*)
Spicy cuttlefish	(*Recipe on page 62*)

METHOD

To assemble the *rojak*
- Put small amounts of each of the ingredients on individual plates, garnish with sliced cucumber and lettuce. Serve sauce (*see recipe below*) separately on the side.

Sauce

INGREDIENTS

Dried chillies	30–40
Onions	2 Tbsp, peeled and chopped
Garlic	1 clove, peeled and finely chopped
Shrimp paste (*belacan*)	1 tsp
Cooking oil	4 Tbsp
Sweet potatoes	400 g (14 oz) boiled, peeled and mashed
Water	560 ml (2^1/$_2$ cups)

Seasoning

Sugar	225–285 g (8–10 oz)
Salt	1^1/$_2$ –2 tsp
Vinegar	2 Tbsp
Tamarind pulp (*asam*)	55 g (2 oz), soaked in 115 ml (^{1}/$_2$ cup) water squeezed and strained
Sesame seeds	30 g (1 oz), toasted, finely ground
Sesame seeds	30 g (1 oz), toasted

METHOD

- Combine dried chillies, chopped onions, garlic and shrimp paste and blend into a fine paste.
- Heat cooking oil in a pan and fry the paste over moderate heat until fragrant. Set aside.
- Put mashed sweet potatoes in a heavy aluminium saucepan. Add 560 ml (2^1/$_2$ cups) water gradually and stir until blended.
- Add the seasoning ingredients, fried paste and the ground sesame seeds. Boil gently for ^{1}/$_2$ hour to thicken, stirring occasionally to prevent sauce from sticking to the bottom of the pan.
- Remove from heat, add the rest of the sesame seeds, stir and set aside to cool.

Coconut Fingers

INGREDIENTS

Plain flour	115 g (4 oz)
Dried prawns	1 Tbsp, soaked to soften and pounded
Salt	1/2 tsp
Sugar	1 tsp
MSG	1/2 tsp, optional
Pepper	1/2 tsp
Chickpea flour	30 g (1 oz)
Coconut	115 g (4 oz), skinned and coarsely grated
Water	115 ml (1/2 cup)
Cooking oil for deep-frying	

METHOD

- Put plain flour, dried prawns, salt, sugar, MSG, if using, and pepper in a bowl and mix well. Add chickpea flour and grated coconut and mix.
- Add water and knead lightly to make a soft dough.
- Shape dough into small 6.5-cm (2 1/2-in) long rolls, tapering at both ends.
- Deep-fry in hot cooking oil for 5 minutes until golden brown and well cooked inside.
- Drain and set aside to cool.

Warday

INGREDIENTS

Eggs	2
Sugar	1 tsp
Salt	1/4 tsp
Pepper	1/2 tsp
MSG	1/4 tsp, optional
Water	85 ml (1/3 cup)
Bicarbonate soda	1/4 tsp
Chickpea flour	85 g (3 oz)
Plain flour	100 g (3 1/2 oz)
Onion	3 Tbsp, chopped
Cooking oil for deep-frying	

METHOD

- Put eggs, sugar, salt, pepper, MSG, if using, and water in a bowl and beat lightly with a fork.
- Put bicarbonate of soda, chickpea flour, plain flour and chopped onion in another bowl. Add in the egg mixture and stir until batter is smooth.
- Divide batter into two portions, setting aside one half to fry the prawn fritters.
- Heat cooking oil in a pan. Drop tablespoonfuls of the remaining batter into the hot oil to fry, allowing space for *warday* to expand. Fry over moderate heat until golden brown.
- Drain in a colander and set aside.

Prawn Fritters

INGREDIENTS

Bicarbonate of soda	$^1/_4$ tsp
Pepper	$^1/_4$ tsp
Salt	A pinch
Self-raising flour	2 Tbsp
Water	2 Tbsp
Warday batter	$^1/_2$ portion (from *warday* recipe – *recipe on page 61*)
Prawns	285 g (10 oz) small, shelled and deveined
Cooking oil for frying	

METHOD

- Combine bicarbonate of soda, pepper, salt and self-raising flour in a bowl and mix.
- Add 2 Tbsp water and *warday* batter and stir until smooth.
- Drop prawns into the batter to coat.
- Fry prawns over moderately high heat until golden brown. Set aside.

Spicy Cuttlefish

INGREDIENTS

Coconut	115 g (4 oz), skinned and grated
Chilli powder	1 Tbsp
Candlenut	1
Shallots	4, peeled
Shrimp paste (*belacan*)	1 tsp
Cuttlefish	1 large, soaked in alkaline water (*recipe on page 13*)
Cooking oil	6 Tbsp
Sugar	1 tsp
MSG	$^1/_2$ tsp, optional
Pepper	$^1/_2$ tsp
Ground cumin	$^1/_2$ tsp

METHOD

- Place grated coconut in a piece of muslin and squeeze to extract No.1 milk. Collect milk and set aside.
- Combine chilli powder, candlenut, shallots and shrimp paste and pound to a fine paste. Set aside.
- Cut cuttlefish into small pieces and pat dry with kitchen towel.
- Heat cooking oil in a wok. When very hot, fry the cuttlefish – a few pieces at a time – for 1 minute. Set aside.
- In the same wok, heat cooking oil and fry spice paste until fragrant and oil bubbles through.
- Add coconut milk, sugar, MSG, if using, pepper and ground cumin, stir and continue cooking over moderate heat until dry.
- Return cuttlefish to the wok, stir and cook over gentle heat. Remove and set aside.

noodles

EVERYDAY FAVOURITES: THE BEST OF SINGAPORE'S RECIPES

Char Kway Teow

FRIED RICE NOODLES

INGREDIENTS

Water	6 Tbsp
Salt	1 tsp
MSG	$1/2$ tsp, optional
Lard or cooking oil	8 Tbsp
Garlic	2 tsp, peeled and pounded
Bean sprouts	310 g (11 oz), picked, washed and drained
Flat rice noodles (*kway teow*)	310 g (11 oz), fresh
Dark soy sauce	2 Tbsp
Eggs	4, beaten
Chilli sauce	(*See recipe below*)
Chinese sausages	2, thinly sliced and fried
Cockles	115 g (4 oz), shelled
Chinese chives	55 g (2 oz), cut into 5-cm (2-in) lengths
Sweet thick black sauce (*kicap pekat manis*)	1–2 Tbsp

METHOD

- In a bowl, combine water, salt and MSG, if using. Set aside.
- Heat a large wok until smoking. Add 4 Tbsp lard or cooking oil and fry garlic until light brown. Add bean sprouts and rice noodles. Add in the salt-MSG mixture, dark soy sauce and stir-fry for $1/2$ minute.
- Push rice noodle mixture to one side of wok. Add the remaining 4 Tbsp lard or cooking and the eggs. Scramble the eggs quickly.
- Stir the scrambled eggs into the noodles and mix well.
- Pour in chilli sauce to taste.
- Add Chinese sausages and stir-fry for another minute. Add some lard to sides of wok if necessary.
- Create a well in the centre of the noodles and add the cockles. Cover cockles with the hot noodles, add chives and sweet thick black sauce. Toss for $1/2$ minute to combine well, then serve on a large serving plate.

Note:
Fry the noodles in two parts if the wok is not large enough. Fry over very high heat to keep the bean sprouts crunchy. For flavour, lard is preferable to cooking oil.

Chilli Sauce

INGREDIENTS

Lard	1 Tbsp
Garlic	1 Tbsp, peeled and chopped
Shrimp paste (*belacan*)	$3/4$ tsp, crumbled
Red chillies	285 g (10 oz), finely blended
Water	340 ml ($1 1/2$ cups)
Salt	$1 1/2$ Tbsp
Sugar	1 Tbsp
Pepper	1 tsp
MSG	1 tsp, optional

METHOD

- Heat lard or cooking oil in a small saucepan and fry garlic and shrimp paste until brown.
- Add blended chillies, water, salt, sugar, MSG, if using, and pepper and bring to a boil.
- Boil gently for a further 5 minutes. Cool and use as required.

Note:
Chilli sauce can be stored in the freezer for future use. Cool completely before pouring it into a plastic container for storing.

Yong Tau Fu

INGREDIENTS

Cooking oil	115 ml ($^1/_2$ cup)
Stuffed triangular bean curd (*taukwa*) (ready-to-use)	20 pieces
Stuffed bittergourd (ready-to-use)	10 slices
Rice vermicelli (*bee hoon*)	900 g (2 lbs)
Water convolvulus (*kangkung*)	900 g (2 lbs), washed and picked
Fish ball (ready-to-use)	60 pieces
Stuffed triangular bean curd puff (*taupok*) (ready-to-use)	30 pieces
Stuffed square bean curd puff (*taupok*) (ready-to-use)	30 pieces
Stuffed green chillies (ready-to-use)	10
Stuffed red chillies (ready-to-use)	10
Spring onions	4, coarsely chopped

Soup

Water	3.5 litres (15$^1/_2$ cups)
Ginger	20 g ($^1/_2$ oz), peeled and crushed
Garlic	6 cloves, peeled and lightly crushed
Anchovies (*ikan bilis*)	170 g (6 oz), washed and drained
Chicken stock cube	1
Salt	1–2 tsp
MSG	2 tsp, optional
Sugar	1 tsp

METHOD

- Make the soup: Place all the soup ingredients in a pot and bring to a boil. Keep boiling over moderate heat for 1$^1/_2$ hours. Strain and set aside.
- Now prepare the rest of the dish. Pour cooking oil into a wok and heat. When hot, add the stuffed triangular bean curd and fry until light brown on all sides. Transfer to a plate.
- Drain off the oil leaving about 2 Tbsp in the wok. When hot, add stuffed bittergourd and fry over low heat for about 2 minutes on each side. Add about 55 ml ($^1/_4$ cup) water, cover the wok and cook for 5 minutes. Remove bittergourd and set aside.
- Bring a pot of water to a boil and add rice vermicelli. Boil for 2–3 minutes, then transfer vermicelli to a basin of cold water. Drain and set aside.
- In another saucepan of water, add 1 tsp each of salt, sugar and cooking oil and bring to a rapid boil. Add water convolvulus and boil rapidly for $^1/_2$ minute. Remove and immerse in cold water for 15 minutes. Drain and set aside.
- Bring the soup to a boil again. Add the fish balls and remove when they float to the surface. Add the stuffed bean curd puffs and boil for 5 minutes. Remove and set aside. Add the stuffed green and red chillies together with 1 tsp cooking oil and boil for 2 minutes. Remove and set aside.
- Serve individually. Place a little rice vermicelli, water convolvulus and a few pieces of the *yong tau foo*, fish balls, chillies and bittergourd in individual bowls.
- Pour hot soup over it and garnish with a little spring onions.
- Serve with chilli sauce and sweet red sauce on the side.

Laksa Lemak

INGREDIENTS

Cooking oil	225 ml (1 cup)
Lemon grass	2 stalks, bruised
Bean sprouts	625 g (1 lb 6 oz), picked, boiled and drained
Coarse rice vermicelli (*bee hoon*)	1.2 kg (2 lb 11 oz)

Rempah

Turmeric	1 Tbsp, peeled
Galangal	1/2 teacup, peeled and sliced
Dried chillies	20
Red chillies	5
Candlenuts	6, crushed
Shrimp paste (*belacan*)	2 Tbsp
Shallots	225 g (8 oz), peeled
Ground coriander or seeds	1 Tbsp

Coconut Milk

Coconut	1.2 kg (2 lb 11 oz), grated
Water	2.7 litres (12 cups)

For Prawns

Water	455 ml (2 cups)
Salt	1 tsp
Sugar	1 tsp
Prawns	445 g (1 lb)

Seasoning

Dried prawns	55 g (2 oz), pounded
Sugar	1 Tbsp
Salt	2 Tbsp

Garnish

Fish cake	8 pieces, fried and sliced into thin strips
Cucumbers	3, skinned, seeded and sliced lengthwise
Polygonum leaves (*laksa* leaves or *daun kesum*)	55 g (2 oz), finely sliced

METHOD

- Grind *rempah* ingredients to a fine paste.
- Using a piece of muslin, squeeze grated coconut for No.1 milk and collect in a bowl. Add 2.7 litres (12 cups) water to grated coconut and squeeze again to extract No.2 milk. Collect in a separate container and set aside.
- To prepare prawns: Boil the 455 ml (2 cups) water in a saucepan with salt and sugar. Add the prawns and cook for about 5–7 minutes. Remove prawns, shell and slice lengthwise. Set aside.
- Return shells to saucepan, boil for 10 minutes and strain liquid for stock.
- To prepare gravy: Heat cooking oil in a wok and fry *rempah* paste and lemon grass until fragrant and the oil separates.
- Add No.2 milk and prawn stock and bring to a boil. Add seasoning ingredients and boil for 10 minutes over low heat.
- Reduce the heat and simmer. Add No.1 milk, setting aside 2 Tbsp for the chilli paste (*recipe on page 71*). Stir for a minute then remove from heat. Continue stirring to prevent curdling.
- Serve in individual portions. Place some bean sprouts and rice vermicelli in bowls. Add hot gravy and garnish with prepared prawns, fish cake, cucumber, polygonum leaves and chilli paste (*recipe on page 71*).

Note:
Cellophane noodles (*tang hoon*) can also be added to the rice vermicelli.

This recipe serves 10.

Chilli Paste

INGREDIENTS

Dried chillies	55 g (2 oz)
Red chillies	5
Shrimp paste *(belacan)*	1 tsp
Cooking oil	2 Tbsp
Water	1–2 Tbsp
Sugar	2 tsp
Salt	1 tsp
No.1 coconut milk	2 Tbsp *(reserved from main recipe on page 70)*

METHOD

- Combine red and dried chillies and shrimp paste and grind to a fine paste.
- Heat pan until hot. Heat cooking oil and fry chili paste until well done and oil comes through.
- Add 1–2 Tbsp water, salt, sugar and No.1 coconut milk and fry.
- Transfer to a bowl.

Hae Mee

PRAWN MEE SOUP

INGREDIENTS

Prawns	625 g (1 lb 6 oz)
Pork fat	170 g (6 oz), diced
Cooking oil	2 Tbsp
Water	4.5 litres (20 cups)
Pork ribs	625 g (1 lb 6 oz), cut into pieces
Pig's tail	1, cut into pieces
Lean pork	310 g (11 oz)
Bean sprouts	455 g (1 lb), picked and washed
Water convolvulus (*kangkung*)	310 g (11 oz), cut into moderate lengths
Fresh yellow noodles	620 g (1 lb 6 oz)
Rice vermicelli (*bee hoon*)	310 g (11 oz), scalded

Seasoning

Salt	2 tsp
Sugar	2 tsp
MSG	2 tsp, optional
Peppercorns	1 Tbsp
Soy sauce	2 Tbsp
Dark soy sauce	2 tsp

Garnish

Crisp-fried shallots	55 g (2 oz) (*recipe on page 12*)
Red chillies	5, thinly sliced
Pepper	A dash
Green chillies	5, thinly sliced
Soy sauce	To taste

METHOD

- Wash and drain prawns. Remove heads and set aside.
- Fry pork fat in a pan until brown. Transfer to a bowl and set aside.
- Pour 2 Tbsp cooking oil in a pan and heat. Add prawn heads and stir-fry for 5 minutes until it turns a bright red. Transfer to a bowl and set aside.
- Place 4.5 litres (20 cups) of water in a saucepan and bring to a boil. Add the unshelled prawns and cook for 2 minutes. Remove prawns, shell and slice into halve lengthwise.
- Return prawn shells to the saucepan of water, add pork ribs, pig's tail and lean pork, seasoning ingredients and prawn heads. Cook over a very high heat for 10 minutes. Reduce heat to low and let soup simmer for 1–1^1/$_2$ hours.
- Strain soup. Return pork ribs and pig's tail to soup.
- Slice lean pork and set aside.
- When ready to serve, bring a saucepan of water to a boil and blanch a single serving of bean sprouts, water convolvulus, noodles and rice vermicelli. Drain and place in a bowl.
- Place a few pieces of pork ribs, pig's tail, sliced lean pork and sliced prawns in each bowl and add the hot soup.
- Garnish with crisp-fried shallots, pork fat and oil and crispy fat cubes. Sprinkle with pepper and serve with sliced chillies and soy sauce as a dipping sauce.

Note:
Only very fresh prawns make a sweet soup.

This recipe serves 12.

Kon Loh Mee

NOODLES WITH CHAR SIEW

INGREDIENTS

Anchovies (*ikan bilis*)	115 g (4 oz)
Water	680 ml (3 cups)
Garlic	2 cloves, peeled and lightly crushed
Ginger	10 g, peeled and lightly crushed
Flowering cabbage (*choy sum*)	225 g (8 oz)
Salt	1 tsp
Sugar	1 tsp
Fresh thin egg noodles	8 bundles
Roast pork (*char siew*)	225 g (8 oz), finely sliced

Sauce for One Serving

Chilli sauce	2–3 Tbsp
Peanut oil	1 Tbsp
MSG	$1/2$ tsp, optional
Soy sauce	1 Tbsp
Oyster sauce	1 Tbsp
Sesame oil	$1/2$ tsp
Stock	4–6 Tbsp

METHOD

- In a saucepan, combine anchovies, water, garlic and ginger and bring to a boil for 1 hour. Strain and set aside.
- Wash flowering cabbage, cut into short lengths. In a pot of boiling water, add the salt and sugar and blanch flowering cabbage. Remove vegetable and immerse in cold water for 5 minutes. Drain.
- In a bowl, combine the sauce ingredients for one serving. Set aside.
- To prepare a single serving on the noodles: Bring a large saucepan of water to a boil over high heat. Loosen a bundle of noodles and put it into the boiling water. Stir for 1 minute, then scoop it out.
- Immerse in a basin of cold water for $1/2$ minute. Repeat this process for another $1/4$ minute. Remove and drain.
- Place noodles in a bowl and toss with the sauce.
- Transfer to a serving plate, garnish with flowering cabbage and slices of roast pork. Serve hot.
- Repeat process single servings at a time.

Note:
The noodles used here are the thin variety, quite different from the starchy, thick yellow noodles used in the *hae mee* recipe.

This recipe serves 8.

Loh Mee

INGREDIENTS

Prawns	250 g (9 oz), shelled and deveined (keep shells for stock)
Cooking oil	6 Tbsp
Water	1 litre (4^{1}/$_{2}$ cups)
Squid	200 g (7 oz), cleaned and sliced into thin rings
Spanish mackerel (*ikan tenggiri*)	250 g (9 oz), thickly sliced
Oysters	200 g (7 oz), optional
Garlic	^{1}/$_{2}$ tsp, peeled and chopped
Ginger	10 g, peeled and thinly sliced
Plain flour	3 Tbsp
Bean sprouts	400 g (14 oz), picked, washed and drained
Flowering cabbage (*choy sum*)	200 g (7 oz), cut into short lengths
Fresh flat yellow noodles (*mee pok*)	600 g (1 lb 5 oz)

Marinade

Soy sauce	1 Tbsp
Sugar	1 tsp
Ginger juice	1 tsp

Seasoning

Oyster sauce	3 Tbsp
Thai fish sauce	2 Tbsp
Dark soy sauce	1 Tbsp
Sesame oil	1 tsp
Pepper	^{1}/$_{2}$ tsp
Chicken stock granules	1 tsp

Garnish

Chinese parsley (coriander leaves)	3 sprigs, cut into short lengths
Red chillies	2, seeded, thinly sliced lengthwise
Crisp-fried shallots	6 Tbsp (*recipe on page 12*)

METHOD

- Wash and drain prawn shells. Place 2 Tbsp cooking oil in a pan, add shells and fry.
- Add 1 litre (4^{1}/$_{2}$ cups) water and bring to a boil. Boil until stock is reduced by one-third.
- Combine prawns, squid, mackerel and oysters, if using, and mix with marinade ingredients. Leave for ^{1}/$_{2}$ hour.
- Heat the remaining 4 Tbsp cooking oil in a wok. Add garlic and sliced ginger and fry until light brown.
- Add the flour and stir for ^{1}/$_{2}$ minute. Pour in half of the prawn stock and seasoning ingredients and bring to a boil.
- Pour in remaining stock, add the seafood and cover pan. Bring to a boil.
- Push seafood to a side in the pan, and add the flowering cabbage and bean sprouts. Cook for ^{1}/$_{2}$ minute over high heat, then add in the noodles and cook for approximately 1 minute.
- Transfer noodles to a large serving plate and spoon gravy over. Top with garnish and serve hot.

Mee Goreng

INDIAN-STYLE FRIED NOODLES

INGREDIENTS

Onion	1, peeled and finely sliced
Tomatoes	2, cut into wedges
Cooking oil for frying	
White cabbage	225 g (8 oz), cut into 5-cm (2-in) lengths
Bean sprouts	455 g (1 lb), picked and washed
Fresh yellow noodles	340 g (12 oz)
Potatoes	4, boiled, skinned and cut into wedges
Eggs	4
Soy sauce	To taste
Crisp-fried shallots	2 Tbsp (recipe on page 12)
Kalamansi limes	6, halved

Seasoning

Tomato sauce	2–3 Tbsp
Soy sauce	1–2 Tbsp
Green chillies	4, sliced
Red chillies	4, sliced

METHOD

- Heat iron wok until smoking hot. Add 2 Tbsp cooking oil and fry onion slices until soft and translucent.
- Add in tomatoes and cabbage.
- Add bean sprouts and noodles and stir for 1 minute.
- Add seasoning ingredients and potatoes. Mix well.
- Push noodles to one side of the wok. Add 2 Tbsp cooking oil and scramble eggs (two at a time) with a sprinkling of soy sauce. Mix egg and noodles thoroughly.
- Add gravy (see recipe below) according to taste. Stir mixture over a very high heat for 1 minute. Transfer to a serving plate.
- Garnish with crisp-fried shallots and kalamansi limes.

Note:
Fry noodles over high heat to prevent them from turning soggy and to keep bean sprouts crisp. If your wok is not big enough, fry the noodles in two batches.

Gravy

INGREDIENTS

Onions	225 g (8 oz), peeled
Dried chillies	55 g (2 oz)
Garlic	4 cloves, peeled
Shrimp paste (belacan)	1 Tbsp
Cooking oil	340 ml (1 1/2 cups)
Dried anchovies (ikan bilis)	55 g (2 oz)
Sugar	1 Tbsp
Salt	1 tsp
MSG	1 tsp, optional

METHOD

- Pound together onions, chillies, garlic and shrimp paste to form a fine paste.
- Heat 115 ml (1/2 cup) cooking oil in a pan and fry anchovies over a moderate heat until crisp. Drain and pound coarsely.
- In a clean pan, heat remaining cooking oil. Stir chilli-garlic paste and fry until fragrant and oil bubbles through.
- Add the sugar, salt and MSG, if using, then lower the heat. Add the pounded anchovies and cook for 2–3 minutes. Transfer to a bowl and use as required.
- Store the remainder in a freezer.

Hokkien Mee

INGREDIENTS

Prawns	310 g (11 oz)
Cooking oil	1 Tbsp
Water	680 ml (3 cups)
Salt	1 tsp
MSG	2 tsp, optional
Squid	310 g (11 oz), cartilage and ink bag removed
Streaky pork	310 g (11 oz)
Fresh yellow egg noodles	625 g (1 lb 6 oz)
Eggs	4
Garlic	2 tsp, peeled and pounded
Soy sauce	2 Tbsp
Bean sprouts	625 g (1 lb 6 oz), picked and washed
Lard or cooking oil for frying	8 Tbsp
Chinese chives	55 g (2 oz), cut into 3-cm (1 1/2-in) lengths

Garnish

Kalamansi limes (*limau kesturi*)	4, halved
Red chillies	4, thinly sliced

METHOD

- To make prawn stock: Remove prawn heads. Wash and drain. Fry heads in 1 Tbsp cooking oil for 1 minute. Pound and add in 225 ml (1 cup) water. Strain and set liquid aside.
- In a saucepan, combine the remaining 455 ml (2 cups) water with the salt and MSG, if using, and bring to a boil.
- Add the squid and boil for 2 minutes until opaque and cooked. Remove from the pan, leaving the water in the pan and cut squid into rings. Set aside.
- Bring the water in the pan back to a boil and add in prawns to cook. Remove prawns from pan and shell, leaving tails on. Set aside.

- Bring the water back to a boil and add the streaky pork. Cook until done (about 15 minutes). Let pork cool, then slice into thin strips. Set aside.
- Add the prawn stock into the saucepan with the water in which the prawns, squid and pork had been cooked and continue boiling until liquid is reduced to 455 ml (2 cups). Strain and set aside.

To fry the noodles

- Halve the noodles, eggs, garlic, chives, soy sauce, bean sprouts, the cooked prawns, pork and squid. These are to be fried in two separate batches.
- Add 2 Tbsp lard or cooking oil to a heated wok to fry one batch of the above ingredients. When the lard or cooking oil is hot, add eggs and scramble, then add bean sprouts and noodles. Add 1 Tbsp of stock to the noodles, stir-fry a moment and cover the wok for a few minutes.
- Now add the prawns, pork and squid, cover the wok and leave to cook a further 2 minutes. Then toss the noodles over high heat for a short while.
- Push the noodle mixture to one side of the wok. Add 2 Tbsp lard or cooking oil to the center of the wok and add the garlic. Fry until light brown. Add the light soy sauce and a ladleful of stock. Stir in noodle mixture and toss.
- Add chives and toss to mix.
- Transfer noodles to a plate, garnish with limes and chillies and serve hot.
- Repeat the process with the other batches of the ingredients.

Note
Traditionally, lard is the preferred choice for frying Hokkien mee as it imparts a richer flavour than ordinary cooking oil. Frying should be done over high heat throughout to prevent the noodles from becoming soggy and to keep the bean sprouts crunchy.

This recipe serves 6.

Mee Rebus

INGREDIENTS

Beef shin	225 g (8 oz), diced
Chicken stock cube	1
Prawn	225 g (8 oz) washed and shelled (keep shells for stock)
Cooking oil	115 ml (1/2 cup)
Fresh yellow egg noodles	680 g (1 1/2 lb)
Bean sprouts	560 g (1 1/4 lb), picked and washed

Rempah

Galangal	18 slices, peeled
Garlic	4 cloves, peeled
Shallots	115 g (4 oz), peeled
Dried chillies	14–20
Turmeric	10 g, peeled
Shrimp paste (belacan)	1 tsp

Seasoning

Yellow bean paste (taucheo)	115 g (4 oz), pounded
MSG	1 tsp, optional
Salt	1–1/2 Tbsp
Sugar	2 Tbsp

Thickening

Sweet potatoes	115 g (4 oz) boiled, skinned and finely mashed
Plain flour	2 Tbsp
Cornflour	2 Tbsp
Water	225 ml (1 cup)

Garnish

Chinese celery	8 sprigs, sliced
Firm bean curd (taukwa)	4 pieces, diced and fried
Green chillies	10, sliced
Red chillies	6, sliced
Crisp-fried shallots	55 g (2 oz) (recipe on page 12)
Kalamansi limes (limau kesturi)	12–14, halved
Eggs	6, hard boiled, shelled and sliced

METHOD

- Combine *rempah* ingredients and grind to a paste.
- Place beef shin, chicken stock cube and 680 ml (3 cups) water and boil over low heat until meat is tender.
- Place prawn shells in a pan with 1 Tbsp cooking oil and fry for 1 minute. Transfer to a bowl and set aside.
- Bring 900 ml (4 cups) water to a boil. Add the prawn shells and boil for 7 minutes. Strain and set aside the stock to make the gravy.
- Pour the rest of the oil into a wok, add *rempah* and fry until fragrant – about 5–7 minutes. Add the seasoning ingredients and stir. Set aside.
- Combine thickening ingredients in a bowl and mix well.
- Place prawns, prawn stock, beef shin and *rempah* paste in a pot and bring to a boil.
- Remove 225 ml (1 cup) of this gravy and combine with thickening mixture. Mix well, then pour it back gradually into the pot of gravy. Stir, then let gravy simmer for 10 minutes.
- Meanwhile prepare the noodles: Scald noodles and bean sprouts in boiling water. Remove the noodles and bean sprouts, drain and place on a serving plate.
- Spoon gravy, prawns and beef over noodles. Garnish. Serve hot.

Note:
This recipe serves 10.

Teochew Kway Teow

RICE NOODLES IN SOUP

INGREDIENTS

Prawns	600 g (1 lb 5 oz) (keep shells for stock)
Sugar	1/2 tsp
Salt	1/4 tsp
Soy sauce	1 tsp
Fish balls (ready-to-use)	40, small
Minced pork	115 g (4 oz), mixed with 4 Tbsp water and 1/2 tsp MSG (optional)
Flat rice noodles (*kway teow*)	600 g (1 lb 5 oz)
Fresh yellow egg noodles	600 g (1 lb 5 oz)
Bean sprouts	600 g (1 lb 5 oz), picked and washed

Stock

Water	3.8 litres (16 1/2 cups)
Salt	1 1/2 Tbsp
MSG	2 tsp, optional
Peppercorns	1 Tbsp
Pork bones	600 g (1 lb 5 oz)

Garnish

Fish cakes	4, fried and thinly sliced
Preserved Tientsin cabbage (*tung chye*)	4 Tbsp
Chinese celery	A handful
Spring onions	
Garlic	4 cloves, peeled, chopped and fried to a light brown with 8 Tbsp lard or cooking oil

Dipping Sauce

Red chillies	8, thinly sliced
Fish sauce	8 Tbsp

METHOD

- Shell prawns except for the tail. Slit prawns lengthwise, to remove the dark veins. Marinade prawns with the sugar, 1/4 tsp salt and soy sauce.
- Make the stock: Pour 3.4 litres (15 cups) of water and the rest of the stock ingredients into a pot and bring to a fast boil for 1/2 hour. Remove scum as it floats to the surface. Add the remaining 400 ml (1 1/2 cups) water and bring to the boil again over high heat. Remove scum as it rises and continue boiling for 1 hour over moderate heat.
- Add prawn shells to the stock and continue boiling for another hour.
- Strain stock into a saucepan. Measure stock to come up to 2.3 litres (10 1/4 cups). Add hot water if necessary and bring it to a boil.
- Add in the prawns to boil over high heat until cooked. Transfer to a plate.
- Add the fish balls and bring to a boil again. Scoop out fish balls when they rise to the surface. Set aside.
- Let stock to simmer until ready to serve.

To serve

- Bring stock to a boil.
- Put minced pork in a bowl and add 455 ml (2 cups) of the boiling stock. Stir to separate meat, cover and set aside.
- Divide noodles and bean sprouts into 8 individual portions.
- Put some water into another saucepan and bring to a boil.
- Add an individual portion of the noodles and bean sprouts into the saucepan of boiling water and boil for 20 seconds. Remove, drain and place in a serving bowl. Pour in enough of the stock to just cover the noodles and add some of the minced pork. Repeat process with the rest of the noodles.
- Top with garnish ingredients including 1/2–1 Tbsp of the fried garlic and oil. Add a dash of pepper and serve immediately. Combine chillies and fish sauce and serve in a separate saucer.

Note:
Using fish sauce together with the sliced chillies adds a sweeter flavour. If unavailable, substitute with light soy sauce.
When frying garlic, lard is preferable to cooking oil as it imparts a delicate aroma to this dish. Without the lard, this dish would be incomplete. This recipe serves 8.

Mee Siam

INGREDIENTS

Rice Vermicelli

Shallots	225 g (8 oz), peeled
Dried chillies	50–60
Shrimp paste (*belacan*)	2 Tbsp
Cooking oil for frying	
Dried prawns	3 Tbsp, soaked to soften and finely pounded
Water	400 ml (1³/₄ cups)
Salt	1 Tbsp
Sugar	3 Tbsp
MSG	1 tsp, optional
Bean sprouts	1.2 kg (2 lb 11 oz), picked, washed and drained
Rice vermicelli (*bee hoon*)	625 g (1¹/₂ lb), briefly soaked in hot water and drained

Garnish

Hard-boiled eggs	12, shelled and wedged or sliced
Firm bean curd (*taukwa*)	4 pieces, diced and fried
Prawns	625 g (1 lb 6 oz), shelled and deveined, fried and halved lengthwise
Chinese chives	115 g (4 oz), cut into 2.5-cm (1-in) lengths
Kalamansi limes (*limau kesturi*)	310 g (11 oz), halved

METHOD

- Pound shallots, dried chillies and shrimp paste together to make a fine paste.
- Heat cooking oil in wok and fry dried prawns for 1 minute. Add chilli-shallot paste and fry until fragrant and oil separates. Set aside 3 Tbsp of this fried paste and some oil for cooking the gravy (*see recipe below*) later.
- Add water, salt, sugar and MSG, if using, into the wok with the remaining chilli-shallot paste and simmer.
- Add the bean sprouts and stir-fry for 1 minute. Push bean sprouts to one side of the wok.
- Add rice vermicelli and stir-fry over high heat. Toss until the liquid is absorbed.
- Push bean sprouts back into the rice vermicelli and mix.
- Reduce heat, stir and cook until rice vermicelli is dry and fluffy.
- Transfer to cool on a large plate.

To serve

- Place rice vermicelli on a large serving plate or on individual dinner plates.
- Pour gravy (*see recipe below*) over the vermicelli, add garnish ingredients and serve with the sambal (*see recipe on page 87*) on the side.

Gravy

INGREDIENTS

Yellow bean paste (*taucheo*)	8 Tbsp, finely pounded
Sugar	6 Tbsp
Onions	2, peeled and thinly sliced
Tamarind pulp (*asam*)	2 Tbsp, mixed with 225 ml (1 cup) water, squeezed and strained
Water	1.8 litres (8 cups)

METHOD

- Place yellow bean paste, sugar, onions and tamarind water in a saucepan and bring to a boil. Let simmer for ³/₄ hour.
- Add 3 Tbsp of the fried chilli-shallot paste and oil (*from the recipe above*) and boil for 5 minutes. Remove from heat.

Sambal

INGREDIENTS

Dried chilli	40 g, or 10 Tbsp dried chilli paste (*recipe on page 13*)
Shrimp paste (*belacan*)	1 tsp
Cooking oil	8 Tbsp
Onion	1, peeled and finely chopped
Salt	1 tsp
Sugar	2 Tbsp
Tamarind pulp (*asam*)	1 Tbsp, mixed with 125 ml (½ cup) water, squeezed and strained

METHOD

- In a mortar and pestle, combine dried chillies and shrimp paste and pound until fine.
- Heat cooking oil in a wok and fry chopped onion until softened and slightly brown. Add the pounded paste and fry over a moderate heat until fragrant.
- Add salt, sugar and half of the tamarind water. Stir-fry for 1 minute, add the rest of the tamarind water and cook for another 2 minutes, stirring constantly. Transfer to a bowl.

Fried Vegetarian Rice Vermicelli

INGREDIENTS

Rice vermicelli (*bee hoon*)	285 g (10 oz)
Peanut oil or corn oil	6 Tbsp
White cabbage	225 g (8 oz), thinly shredded
French beans	170 g (6 oz), shredded diagonally
Carrots	200 g (7 oz), peeled and grated
Sugar	To taste
Salt	To taste
Garlic	1 tsp, peeled and pounded
Ginger	6 slices, peeled
Dried sweet bean curd strips (*tau kee*)	8 pieces, thinly sliced
Dried Chinese mushrooms	6, pre-soaked and thinly sliced
Prepared gluten (mock duck or mock abalone)	1 can (285 g/10 oz), thinly sliced

Seasoning

Water	340 ml (1¹/₂ cups)
Salt	1 Tbsp, or to taste
MSG	2 Tbsp, optional
Sugar	3 Tbsp
Dark soy sauce	2 tsp
Soy sauce	2 Tbsp
Pepper	1 tsp
Sesame oil	2 tsp

Garnish

Crisp-fried shallots	4 Tbsp (*recipe on page 12*)
Dried sweet bean curd strips (*tau kee*)	4 pieces, cut into matchstick size and fried to a crisp
Sesame seeds	4 Tbsp, roasted

METHOD

- In a large bowl, immerse rice vermicelli in boiling water for 3 minutes and drain in a colander. Rinse it under running tap water for a moment and drain. Set aside for ¹/₂ hour.
- Heat an iron wok, then add 2 Tbsp peanut or corn oil.
- When oil is hot, fry cabbage, French beans and carrots separately for a minute. For each of the vegetables, sprinkle a little water and add a pinch of sugar and salt and a little oil. Toss to mix and set aside.
- In the same wok, heat the remaining 4 Tbsp oil and fry garlic and ginger until light brown and fragrant. Add the dried sweet bean curd and mushrooms and fry for a minute.
- Add the sliced gluten and seasoning ingredients. Bring to the boil for 3 minutes.
- Add rice vermicelli into the wok and toss in the pan until the gravy is absorbed. Add the vegetables and stir to mix. (*Note*: If the vermicelli is not soft and tender enough, sprinkle a little hot water into the pan to soften. Do not stir too much or vermicelli will break into short strips.)
- Remove vermicelli to a large serving plate, top with garnish ingredients and serve.

Note:
Fry dried sweet bean curd in hot oil over low heat until it blisters, then quickly pour into a steel colander to drain. Spread onto an absorbent paper towel to cool. Keep in an airtight container until ready to serve.

classic combinations

EVERYDAY FAVOURITES – THE BEST OF SINGAPORE'S RECIPES

Chicken Rice

The Chicken

INGREDIENTS

Chicken	1.6 kg (3¹/₂ lb), whole
Garlic	6–8 cloves, peeled and lightly crushed
Ginger	40 g (1¹/₂ oz), peeled and lightly crushed
Spring onions	4, knotted
Water	2 litres (9 cups)
Cucumber	2, sliced
Tomatoes	4, sliced
Chinese parsley (coriander leaves)	2 sprigs, chopped

METHOD

- Wash chicken and rub some salt over it to season.
- Stuff chicken cavity with garlic, ginger and spring onions.
- Put 2 litres (9 cups) of water into a saucepan with 1 tsp salt and bring to a boil over high heat.
- Place chicken in the saucepan and leave uncovered.
- Bring the water back to a boil again for a further 2 minutes, then reduce the heat to as low as possible, cover and let simmer for 25–30 minutes. (Keep the lid on throughout the cooking time).
- Remove chicken from the stock and immerse chicken in a basin of cold water for 5 minutes to stop the cooking process.
- Meanwhile, set aside 1 litre (4¹/₂ cups) of the chicken stock – ie. the liquid in which the chicken was cooked in – for the rice.
- Transfer the chicken to a large plate and brush over with cooking oil. Remove stuffing and leave to cool.
- Cut chicken and arrange on a serving plate.
- Garnish with tomatoes, cucumber and Chinese parsley.

The Rice

INGREDIENTS

Thai fragrant rice	625 g (1 lb 6 oz)
Lard or cooking oil	115 ml (¹/₂ cup)
Chicken stock	1 litre (4¹/₂ cups) (from cooking the chicken)
Salt	2 tsp
MSG	1 tsp, optional
Screwpine (*pandan*) leaves	6, knotted

METHOD

- Wash rice until water runs clear. Drain.
- Heat the lard or cooking oil in a frying pan or wok. When hot, add the rice and toss for 2 minutes.
- In a saucepan, combine the chicken stock, MSG, if using, and salt. Add the rice and screwpine leaves and bring to a boil over moderate heat until all the stock is absorbed.
- Reduce heat to low and cook for a further 15 minutes. Rake rice with a fork and serve hot.

Note:
If you are using a rice cooker, follow the recipe above until after the rice has been tossed in the lard. At this point, combine all the ingredients in the rice cooker and turn it on. When the rice is cooked, wipe moisture from the underside of the cooker lid to prevent the rice from turning soggy.

This recipe serves 8.

Ginger Sauce

INGREDIENTS

Chicken stock	55 ml (¹/₄ cup)
Salt	¹/₂ tsp
MSG	¹/₂ tsp, optional
Sugar	¹/₂ tsp
Ginger	40 g, peeled

METHOD

- Slice ginger thinly and pound until fine.
- Place all the ingredients in a bowl and stir. Serve in a bowl.

Chilli Sauce

INGREDIENTS

Red chillies	10–12
Salt	¹/₂ tsp
Water	55 ml (¹/₄ cup), warm
Lime juice	2–3 Tbsp

METHOD

- Scald chillies with hot water. Remove and drain.
- Remove stems from the chillies. Combine chillies and salt and pound coarsely.
- Transfer to a bowl, add the 55 ml (¹/₂ cup) warm water and lime juice and mix well. Serve.

Nasi Lemak

COCONUT RICE

INGREDIENTS

Rice	680 g (1¹/₂ lb), preferably long-grain Thai rice
Coconut	625 g (1 lb 6 oz), skinned and grated
Water	455 ml (2 cups)
Salt	1¹/₂ tsp
Screwpine (*pandan*) leaves	6, knotted

METHOD

- Wash the rice and soak it in water for 2 hours. Drain.
- While rice is soaking, extract the coconut milk. Place grated coconut in a piece of muslin and squeeze to extract 225 ml (1 cup) No.1 milk. Collect and set aside.
- Add the 455 ml water (2 cups) to the grated coconut and squeeze again to extract No.2 milk. Collect in a separate bowl and add water to No.2 milk to make a total volume of 740 ml (3¹/₄ cups).
- Place rice in an electric rice cooker, stir in the No.2 milk and the salt. Turn it on and cook until done.
- Place the screwpine leaves on top of the rice and cover. Leave the rice in the cooker at 'keep warm' mode for a further ¹/₂ hour. Do not stir.
- Rake the rice with a fork, add the No.1 milk and toss lightly to mix.
- Leave the rice in the cooker to absorb the milk for another 20 minutes, then serve.

Note
Serve *nasi lemak* with crispy anchovies with sambal (*see recipe on page 96*), otak-otak rhio (*see recipe on page 97*), sambal udang (*see recipe on page 96*) and sambal kangkung (*see recipe below*).

This recipe serves 10.

Spicy Sambal Kangkung

INGREDIENTS

Water convolvulus (*kangkung*)	455 g (1 lb)
Lard or cooking oil	4 Tbsp
Red chillies	3
Shrimp paste (*belacan*)	1 Tbsp
Sugar	2 tsp
Salt	A pinch
Dried prawns	2 tsp, soaked to soften and pounded

METHOD

- Cut the water convolvulus into 7.5-cm (3-in) lengths, omitting the tough stalks and roots. Wash thoroughly and drain in a colander.
- Pound red chillies and shrimp paste to a fine paste.
- Heat an iron wok, put in 3 Tbsp cooking oil to fry the chilli paste for ¹/₂ minute. Add the water convolvulus, sugar, salt and dried prawns.
- Stir-fry over high heat for 1 minute. Toss the water convolvulus in the wok to ensure that it is well cooked.
- Add the remaining tablespoon of lard or cooking oil, stir well and remove to a serving plate. Serve immediately.

Crispy Anchovies with Sambal

INGREDIENTS

Coconut	170 g (6 oz), grated
Water	225 ml (1 cup)
Cooking oil	170 ml (³/₄ cup)
Sugar	4 Tbsp
Salt	¹/₄ tsp
MSG	1 tsp, optional
Tamarind pulp *(asam)*	1 Tbsp, mixed with 4 Tbsp water, squeezed and strained
Anchovies	455 g (1 lb)
Cooking oil for deep-frying	

Rempah

Dried chillies	115 g (4 oz), washed, soaked to soften and drained
Garlic	1 clove, peeled
Shallots	115 g (4 oz), peeled
Shrimp paste *(belacan)*	55 g (2 oz)

METHOD

- Make the *sambal*: Combine *rempah* ingredients and blend or pound to a fine paste. Set aside.
- In a bowl, combine grated coconut with 225 ml (1 cup) water. Place handfuls in a piece of muslin and squeeze to extract No. 2 milk. Collect and set aside.
- Heat cooking oil in a wok, then add the *rempah* paste and one-third of the coconut milk. Fry over moderate heat until fragrant.
- Add sugar, salt, MSG, if using, and the tamarind water and stir. Add the remaining coconut milk, lower the heat and simmer for 2 minutes. Transfer to a bowl and set aside.
- Now make the anchovies: Remove heads of the anchovies, then wash and drain them.
- Place cooking oil for deep-frying in a wok and heat until very hot. Deep-fry the anchovies over moderate heat until light brown and crispy. (Lower heat at the end of cooking time to prevent it from turning too dark.)
- Transfer anchovies to a paper towel and cool slightly. Store in an airtight container.
- To serve: mix *sambal* and anchovies and serve.

Sambal Udang

INGREDIENTS

Prawns	600 g (1 lb 5 oz), medium sized, shelled and deveined
Salt	A pinch
Sugar	¹/₂ tsp
Frozen dried chilli paste	115 g (4 oz), thawed *(recipe on page 13)*
Salt	¹/₂ tsp
Sugar	1 tsp
MSG	¹/₂ tsp
Tamarind pulp *(asam)*	1 tsp, mixed with 85 ml (3 fl oz) water squeezed and strained
Coconut	115 g (4 oz), grated and squeezed to obtain 3 Tbsp No.1 milk

METHOD

- Season prawns with pinch of salt and ¹/₂ tsp sugar and set aside.
- Heat an aluminium wok. Put in frozen dried chilli paste, and cook over low heat until oil bubbles through (1¹/₂ minutes).
- Add the rest of the ingredients except the prawns and cook until the mixture comes to the boil.
- Add prawns and stir in pan until prawns are cooked, about 3–4 minutes. Serve hot or cold.

Otak-Otak Rhio

INGREDIENTS

Coconut	570 g (1 1/4 lb), grated
Spanish mackerel (*ikan tenggiri*)	1.2 kg (2 lb 11 oz)
Salt	A pinch
Cooking oil	6 Tbsp
Eggs	4
Kaffir lime leaves (*daun limau purut*)	6, finely sliced
Turmeric leaf (*daun kunyit*)	1, finely sliced
Banana leaves (*daun pisang batu*)	24, or aluminium foil, 21 cm x 22 cm (8 in x 8 1/2 in)

Rempah

Galangal	85 g (3 oz), sliced
Candlenuts	6, crushed
Shrimp paste (*belacan*)	1 tsp
Shallots	340 g (12 oz), peeled
Dried chillies	30–40 g (1–1 1/2 oz), soaked in warm water and drained

Seasoning

Sugar	4 tsp
MSG	2 tsp, optional
Pepper	1/2 tsp
Salt	2 tsp

METHOD

- Place grated coconut in a piece of muslin and squeeze to extract No. I milk. Set aside.
- Combine *rempah* ingredients and pound to a fine paste. Set aside.
- Slice the fish lengthwise and remove bones. Slice the meat from half the fish and set aside.
- Pound or mince the other half of the fish meat until smooth, add a pinch of salt and 6 Tbsp of coconut milk. Place in a bowl and mix until well blended.
- In a heated wok, add 4 Tbsp cooking oil and fry *rempah* paste over moderate heat until fragrant.
- Add seasoning ingredients and 12 Tbsp coconut milk. Cook over low heat until paste is almost dry. Stir frequently to prevent burning. Set aside to cool.
- In a large mixing bowl, combine the minced fish, fried *rempah* paste, eggs, lime and turmeric leaves. Add the sliced fish and remaining 2 Tbsp cooking oil. Mix lightly with a wooden spoon.
- If using banana leaves, wash them and place in a saucepan of boiling water. Blanch for 1/2 minute to soften. Drain.
- Put 2–3 Tbsp of the fish mixture in the centre of each leaf or foil, fold short sides of the leaf to cover the mixture, then overlap the longer sides to form a neat rectangular packet. Staple both ends of the leaf to seal before cooking.
- To grill: Place the packets of *otak-otak* under a preheated grill and cook for 5–7 minutes.
- You can also dry fry it: Place *otak-otak* packages in a very hot wok and fry over moderate heat for 5–6 minutes on each side.
- Transfer to a rack and cool before serving.

Nasi Lontong with Sayur Loday

RICE CAKES WITH VEGETABLES IN COCONUT GRAVY

Sayur Loday

INGREDIENTS

Coconut	625 g (1 lb 6 oz), grated
Firm bean curd (*taukwa*)	6, cut into quarters and fried
Green brinjals	300 g (11 oz), wedged, soaked in salt water and drained before use
Cooking oil	
Garlic	2 cloves, peeled and thinly sliced
Shallots	8, peeled and thinly sliced
Dried chilli paste	2 Tbsp (*recipe on page 13*)
White cabbage	625 g (1 lb 6 oz), sliced
Long beans	625 g (1 lb 6 oz), cut into short lengths
Jicama (*bangkuang* or yam bean)	300 g (11 oz), peeled and cut into thick strips
Dried prawns	4 Tbsp, finely pounded

Rempah (pound into a fine paste)

Shallots	115 g (4 oz), peeled
Garlic	1 clove, peeled
Shrimp paste (*belacan*)	1¹/₂ Tbsp
Turmeric	1 Tbsp, peeled
Candlenuts	2
Dried chillies	5, or 1 Tbsp dried chilli paste (*recipe on page 13*)

Seasoning

Salt	1 Tbsp
Sugar	3 Tbsp
MSG	1 tsp, optional

METHOD

- Add 225 ml (1 cup) water to the grated coconut. Place coconut in a piece of muslin and squeeze to extract No.1 milk. Collect and set aside.
- Add another 2 litres (8³/₄ cups) water to the grated coconut and squeeze again for No.2 milk. Pour into a saucepan.
- Add *rempah* paste, seasoning, cabbage, long beans, jicama and dried prawns. Bring to a gentle boil for ¹/₂ hour.
- Add the bean curd and brinjals and cook for another 5–7 minutes. Remove from heat.
- Heat 6 Tbsp cooking oil and fry the sliced garlic and shallots until light brown. Add chilli paste and stir-fry for ¹/₂ minute.
- Add in No.1 milk and stir while you bring it back to a boil.
- Return the vegetables to the saucepan for another 2–3 minutes. Transfer to a bowl and serve with *nasi lontong* and *sambal goreng* (*recipes on page 100*).

Nasi Lontong

INGREDIENTS

Rice	625 g (1 lb 6 oz), preferably long-grain Thai rice
Salt	¹/₂ tsp
Screwpine (*pandan*) leaves	6, knotted
Water	1.2 litres (5¹/₃ cups)

METHOD

- Wash and soak the rice overnight. Drain before use.
- Wet two 10 cm x 20-cm (4 in x 8-in) cloth bags and fill each with half the rice. Stitch to seal the open end.
- Boil 1.2 litres (5¹/₃ cups) water in a heavy bottomed saucepan.
- Add salt, screwpine leaves and the cloth bags of rice in the saucepan. The water should immerse the bags completely and generously. Boil for 2 hours and remove. (Top up with boiling water when necessary.)
- Wrap the bags in a dry towel and place a bread board and a weight on top. Leave until the rice is firm and completely cool, at least 8–10 hours.
- Remove the stitches of the bags and remove the rice. Cut rice roll into long strips with a wet knife and again into thin squares.

Note:
It is best to cook the rice at night and leave it pressed overnight. Place an enamel plate in the saucepan before putting in the bag of rice to prevent it from sticking to the pan.

Nasi Lontong also can also be cooked in specially-made aluminium tubes (*see picture on the left*). The tubes can be purchased from shops selling cooking and baking equipement. Line the inside of the tube with banana leaf, half fill with the rice, cover and boil for 2 hours.

Sambal Goreng

INGREDIENTS

Beef liver	225 g (8 oz), cubed
Salt	1/2 tsp
MSG	1/2 tsp, optional
Shrimp paste *(belacan)*	1 tsp
Dried chillies	6
Coconut	285 g (10 oz), grated
Water	170 ml (3/4 cup)
Cooking oil for frying	
Garlic	4 slices, peeled and thinly sliced
Shallots or onions	55 g, peeled and thinly sliced
Red chillies	3, seeded and thinly sliced
Galangal	1 thick piece, peeled and crushed
Prawns	285 g (10 oz), shelled and cleaned
Firm bean curd *(taukwa)*	2 large pieces, cut into small cubes and fried
Fermented soy bean cake *(tempe)*	2 pieces, diced and fried

METHOD

- Season beef liver with salt and MSG, if using. Set aside.
- Combine shrimp paste and dried chilli and pound to a fine paste. Place in a bowl and set aside.
- Using a piece of muslin, squeeze grated coconut to extract No. 1 milk. Set aside.
- Add 170 ml (3/4 cup) water to coconut and squeeze again to extract No. 2 milk. Set aside.
- Heat cooking oil in a wok. Fry garlic, shallots or onions and red chillies separately until golden brown. Transfer to a plate.
- Pour away oil, leaving 3 Tbsp. Add seasoned liver and fry for 5–6 minutes until cooked. Transfer to a plate.
- In a clean pan, heat 2 Tbsp cooking oil and fry galangal for 1 minute. Add chilli-shrimp paste mixture and fry over moderate heat for another minute.
- Add half of the No.1 milk and stir until it comes to a boil. Add prawns, bean curd, liver and fermented soy bean cake and cook over low heat for 2 minutes.
- Pour in No. 2 milk and cook for 5 minutes, then add the rest of the No.1 milk, fried shallots, garlic and red chillies. Stir and simmer until gravy is almost dry.
- Serve hot or at room temperature.

Nasi Goreng

INDONESIAN FRIED RICE

INGREDIENTS

Cooking oil	55 ml (¹/₄ cup)
Dried prawns	30 g (1 oz), coarsely pounded
Cooked rice	455 g (1 lb), cooled

Omelette

Eggs	2
Salt	A pinch
Pepper	A pinch
Cooking oil	1 Tbsp

Aromatics

Shallots	55 g (2 oz), peeled and sliced
Red chillies	2, seeded and sliced
Dried chillies	6, seeded and sliced
Candlenut	1, roughly pounded
Shrimp paste (belacan)	1 tsp

Seasoning

Water	55 ml (¹/₄ cup)
MSG	1 tsp, optional
Pepper	¹/₂ tsp
Salt	¹/₂ tsp
Soy sauce	1 tsp

Garnish

Crisp-fried shallots	2 Tbsp (recipe on page 12)
Red chillies	2, seeded and thinly shredded lengthwise

METHOD

- Make the omelette first: Combine all the omelette ingredients except for the cooking oil and beat lightly.
- Add a little cooking oil to a heated pan. When oil is hot, pour in the egg and move the pan to spread the egg over the base. Fry one side only to make a fluffy omelette.
- Remove and let cool. Roll omelette into a cigar shape and slice thickly. Set aside.
- Add the 55 ml (¹/₄ cup) cooking oil to a heated wok. When oil is hot, add the dried prawns and fry until light brown and fragrant.
- Add the aromatics and stir-fry until fragrant. (Small fresh prawns can also be added.)
- Add the rice and sprinkle in the seasoning ingredients. Toss and continue cooking over high heat for 5 minutes.
- Transfer *nasi goreng* to a large serving plate. Garnish and serve.

Nasi Briyani Ayam

YELLOW RICE WITH MILD SPICY CHICKEN

Spicy Chicken

INGREDIENTS

Chicken	1, about 1.6 kg (3¹/₂ lb), quartered
Evaporated milk	170 ml (³/₄ cup)
Lemon juice	1 Tbsp
Water	112 ml (¹/₂ cup)
Ghee	225 g (8 oz), or 112 g (4 oz) butter and 112 ml (¹/₂ cup) cooking oil combined
Shallots	285 g (10 oz), peeled and thinly sliced
Ginger	1 Tbsp, peeled and chopped
Garlic	3 cloves, peeled and chopped
Green chillies	4, chopped
Chilli powder	1 tsp, mixed to a paste with water
Garam masala	1 tsp *(recipe on page 106)*
Mint leaves	A handful, washed and picked
Chinese parsley (coriander leaves)	2 sprigs, including roots, washed and chopped
Tomatoes	2, cut into wedges
Tomato paste	2 Tbsp

Seasoning

Salt	2 tsp
MSG	2 tsp, optional
Sugar	1 tsp

METHOD

- Season chicken with the 1 Tbsp salt and set aside for 1 hour.
- Combine evaporated milk, lemon juice and water in a bowl and set aside.
- Place half the ghee in a large wok and heat. When hot, add the shallots and fry until golden brown. Set aside.
- Combine chopped ginger, garlic and chilli in a wok and fry until fragrant. Add chilli paste and garam masala and fry.
- Add in mint leaves, Chinese parsley, tomato wedges, tomato paste and the seasoning ingredients. Toss, then pour in half of the evaporated milk mixture. Stir-fry until oil bubbles through.
- Now, add the seasoned chicken, fried shallots, the remaining milk mixture and ghee. Cook over high heat for 10 minutes. Reduce heat to low and cook gently until chicken is tender.
- Drain chicken, set aside. Keep the oil to cook the briyani rice *(recipe on page 106)*.

Briyani Rice

INGREDIENTS

Ghee	55 g (2 oz)
Ginger	1 tsp, peeled and chopped
Garlic	1 Tbsp, peeled and chopped
Shallots	4, peeled and thinly sliced
Cinnamon quill	5-cm (2-in) length
Cardamoms	8, whole, lightly crushed
Cloves	6
Basmati rice	600 g (1 lb 5 oz), washed and drained
Water	1.1 litres (4³/₄ cups), hot
Chicken stock	1 cube, or ³/₄ Tbsp
Salt	1¹/₂ tsp
Yellow food colouring	1 tsp
Rose essence	¹/₄ tsp
Water	4 Tbsp

METHOD

- Place ghee in a wok and heat. When hot, add the ginger, garlic and shallots and fry until light brown.
- Add cinnamon, cardamom and cloves and fry briefly.
- Add in the oil (left over from cooking the chicken) and the rice. Stir until the oil is absorbed into the rice.
- Transfer rice to an electric rice cooker.
- Pour in the hot water, chicken stock and salt. Cook until done.
- Meanwhile, combine yellow food colouring, rose essence and water.
- When rice is cooked, remove lid and sprinkle the yellow colouring mixture over rice.
- Cover again and let rice sit for another 10 minutes as the cooker remains on the 'keep warm' mode.
- Remove from heat and fluff the rice, mixing the colours evenly. Serve hot with the spicy chicken.

Garam Masala

INGREDIENTS

Coriander seeds	115 g (4 oz), washed and dried
Cumin seeds	55 g (2 oz), washed and dried
Black peppercorns	2 Tbsp
White peppercorns	1 Tbsp
Cardamom seeds	3 tsp (measured after seeds are removed from pods)
Cinnamon quill	30 g (1 oz), broken into small pieces
Cloves	2 tsp
Nutmegs	3

METHOD

- Combine the ingredients and spread in a single layer on an aluminium tray.
- Heat under a warm grill until fragrant and very lightly browned, but do not allow spices to darken.
- While warm, grind the spices in a coffee or spice grinder until very fine. Keep in an airtight bottle and store in fridge.

Roti Jala with Chicken Curry

LACY PANCAKE AND CHICKEN CURRY

Roti Jala

INGREDIENTS

Milk	225 ml (1 cup)
Eggs	2
Salt	A pinch
Cooking oil	1 Tbsp
Plain flour	115 g (4 oz)

METHOD

- Combine milk, eggs, salt and cooking oil in a bowl and beat.
- Sift flour into a mixing bowl. Add egg mixture and stir until batter is smooth. Strain through a nylon sieve and set aside for 15 minutes.
- Grease a heated frying pan, then pour some batter into the *roti jala* maker (*see picture on the left*). Holding the *roti jala* maker over the pan, run the batter in a lacy pattern over the pan to form a round shape.
- Cook for $1/2$ minute or until batter changes colour. Using a spatula, fold the pancake into quarters and remove from pan. Set aside.
- Repeat until all the batter is used up.
- Stack the pancakes on a plate and cover with a tea towel or aluminium foil to prevent them from drying up.
- Serve hot or at room temperature with chicken curry.

Chicken Curry

INGREDIENTS

Chicken	1.6 kg (3½ lb), chopped
Coconut	115 g (4 oz), grated
Water	225 ml (1 cup)
Cooking oil	115 ml (½ cup)
Shallots	285 g (10 oz), peeled and thinly sliced
Dried chillies	8–10, soaked to soften and ground to a paste
Curry leaves	1 stalk, washed and picked

Marinade

Garlic	10 cloves, peeled
Ginger	1 Tbsp, peeled
Turmeric	½ tsp, peeled
Curry powder	2 Tbsp, mixed with 4 Tbsp water
Salt	1 tsp
MSG	1 tsp, optional

Spice Paste

Cumin seeds	1 heaped Tbsp, or ¾ Tbsp ground cumin
Poppy seeds	1 Tbsp, optional
Cashew nuts	8
Almonds	8

Seasoning

Salt	¾–1 tsp
MSG	1 tsp, optional

METHOD

- Prepare the marinade: combine garlic, ginger, turmeric and curry powder. Pound to a fine paste and mix with salt and MSG, if using.
- Rub marinade all over chicken and leave for ½ hour.
- Meanwhile, combine spice paste ingredients and pound finely. Set aside.
- In a bowl, combine the water and grated coconut. Using a piece of muslin, squeeze coconut to extract No.2 coconut milk. Collect in a bowl.
- Add spice paste to the coconut milk and mix.
- Heat cooking oil in a wok. Add three-quarter of the sliced shallots and fry until light golden brown. Lower heat, add the chillies and curry leaves and fry until oil turns red.
- Now add the chicken and stir. Reduce the heat to moderate and cook in a covered wok for ½ hour.
- Now add the rest of the sliced shallots, the seasoning and the milk mixture. Stir, bring to a boil again, reduce heat and simmer for another 15–20 minutes or until chicken is tender.
- Serve with *roti jala*.

kuih&desserts

EVERYDAY FAVOURITES – THE BEST OF SINGAPORE'S RECIPES

Kuih Lapis Beras

RAINBOW LAYER CAKE

INGREDIENTS

Coconut	680 g (1^1/$_2$ lb), skinned and grated
Water	570 ml (2^1/$_2$ cups)
Wet rice flour	340 g (12 oz) (*recipe on page 13*)
Sago flour	225 g (8 oz)
Salt	^{1}/$_4$ tsp
Sugar	455 g (1 lb), coarse grain
Water	285 ml (1^1/$_4$ cups)
Screwpine (*pandan*) leaves	8, knotted
A variety of food colouring (including dark red colouring)	

METHOD

- Combine grated coconut with the 570 ml (2^1/$_2$ cups) water. Place in a piece of muslin and squeeze to extract No.2 coconut milk. Collect in a bowl.
- Add enough water to the coconut milk to make a total volume of 855 ml (3^3/$_4$ cups).
- In a separate bowl, combine the wet rice flour, sago flour and salt. Add the coconut milk gradually and mix until smooth. Set aside.
- In a saucepan, combine the sugar, the 285 ml (1^1/$_4$ cups) water and screwpine leaves and bring to a boil for 10 minutes over moderate heat. Strain into a bowl.
- Add enough hot water to the syrup to make a total volume of 425 ml (1^3/$_4$ cups).
- Pour the hot syrup gradually into the flour mixture, stirring until well blended.
- Divide the flour mixture into four portions. Set aside one portion to remain uncoloured. Add food colouring to the remaining three portions. Of the uncoloured portion, set aside 140 ml (^{2}/$_3$ cup) and colour it dark red.
- Grease a deep, 18-cm (7-in) cake pan or steaming pan (*see picture on the left*). Place pan in steamer over rapidly boiling water. Pour 140 ml (^{2}/$_3$ cup) of a coloured batter into the pan and steam for 5–6 minutes. This will form one layer. Pour 140 ml (^{2}/$_3$ cup) of a different coloured batter over the first layer and steam again for 5–6 minutes to create a second layer. Repeat the process, alternating the batters, until all the batter is used up. This will create layered, multi-coloured cake.
- Use the dark red batter to make the final layer.
- Leave cake to cool for 7–8 hours. Cut into rectangular pieces and serve.

Note:
Wipe the underside of steamer lid from time to time. It is best to leave the cake overnight before cutting.

Kuih Dadar

COCONUT ROLLS WITH COCONUT SAUCE

INGREDIENTS

Coconut	560 g (1¼ lb), skinned and grated
Water	455 ml (2 cups)
Salt	½ tsp
Eggs	4, lightly beaten
Cooking oil	1 Tbsp
Plain flour	225 g (8 oz)
Sago flour	1 Tbsp
A variety of food colouring	

METHOD

• Place handfuls of grated coconut into a piece of muslin cloth and squeeze to extract 225 ml (1 cup) of No.1 milk. Collect in a bowl and set aside. Add 455 ml (2 cups) water to the grated coconut and using the muslin cloth, squeeze again to obtain 225 ml (1 cup) of No.2 milk. Collect and set aside.

• In a large bowl, combine the No.1 and No.2 coconut milk as well as the salt, eggs, cooking oil, and the two flours. Mix until smooth and strain.

• Divide the batter into three or four portions, depending on the number of food colours you are using. Colour each portion of the batter with several drops of the food colouring. Stir well and leave to stand for ½ hour.

• Heat an omelette pan. When hot, remove pan from the heat and grease its base. Pour just enough batter to cover the base of the pan thinly. Return pan to the heat and fry pancake until the edges curl slightly and pancake is able to slip away from the pan easily.

• Remove and repeat until the batter is used up. Leave to cool.

• Fill each pancake with 2 Tbsp of coconut filling (*see recipe on page 115*). Fold to enclose filling, then roll.

Note:
Use an omelette pan with a 16.5-cm (6½-in) base.

This recipe makes 22 pancakes.

Sauce

INGREDIENTS

Coconut	680 g (1½ lb), skinned and grated
Water	455 ml (2 cups)
Plain flour	3 Tbsp
Wet rice flour	55 g (2 oz) (*recipe on page 13*), or 3 Tbsp rice flour
Salt	1 tsp
Sugar	1 Tbsp
Screwpine (*pandan*) leaves	6, knotted

METHOD

• Using a piece of muslin, squeeze grated coconut to extract No.1 milk. Set aside.

• Add 455 ml (2 cups) water to grated coconut and squeeze again for No.2 milk. Add water to bring it up to a total volume of 855 ml (3¾ cups).

• In a bowl, combine the plain flour, wet rice flour and 225 ml (1 cup) No.2 milk. Stir and set aside.

• Place the rest of the No.2 milk in a saucepan with the salt, sugar and screwpine leaves. Bring it to near boiling point in a saucepan.

• Remove saucepan from the heat. Add the flour mixture gradually to the hot milk, stirring constantly. Then add No.1 milk.

• Return saucepan to the heat and bring the mixture to a gentle boil, stirring constantly.

• Pour sauce into a bowl to cool.

• Serve with the *kuih dadar*.

Coconut Filling

INGREDIENTS

Sugar	3 Tbsp
Palm sugar (gula Melaka)	285 g (10 oz), grated
Water	3 Tbsp
Screwpine (pandan) leaves	6, knotted
Coconut	560 g (20 oz), skinned and grated
Sago flour	1 Tbsp, mixed with 2 Tbsp water

METHOD

- Combine the sugar, palm sugar, water and screwpine leaves in a wok and heat until sugar is syrupy.
- Add grated coconut and lower the heat. Stir mixture until it is almost dry.
- Add the sago flour mixture and stir thoroughly. Cook for another 5 minutes, then leave to cool.

Coconut Candy

INGREDIENTS

Evaporated milk	115 ml ($^1/_2$ cup)
Condensed milk	2 Tbsp
Sugar	340 g (12 oz)
Salt	1 tsp
Coconut	390 g (14 oz), skinned and grated
Vanilla essence	1 tsp
Butter	1 tsp
A variety of food colouring	A few drops

METHOD

- In a bowl, combine evaporated milk and condensed milk.
- Place sugar, salt and the combined milk in a wok and stir over low heat until sugar is dissolved.
- Add the grated coconut and continue cooking until almost dry, about 2 hours. Stir often to prevent burning.
- Remove from the heat and add vanilla essence and butter. Mix well to incorporate.
- Divide coconut mixture into portions and colour each portion with your choice of food colouring.
- Grease baking trays and fill with coconut mixture. Press down firmly with a plastic sheet and leave to cool.
- Turn out the candy and cut before it completely dries out and hardens.
- Leave to cool completely then store.

Apom Berkuah

INGREDIENTS

Coconut	1.6 kg (3$^{1}/_2$ lb), grated
Water	1.1 litres (4$^{3}/_4$ cups)
Dried yeast	$^{3}/_4$ tsp, or 1$^{1}/_2$ tsp fresh yeast
Plain flour	4 Tbsp
Castor sugar	1 tsp
Coconut water	5 Tbsp
Rice flour	340 g (12 oz)
Glutinous rice flour	2 Tbsp
Fine salt	1 level tsp
Cold water	310 ml (1$^{1}/_3$ cups)
Coconut water	285 ml (1$^{1}/_4$ cups)
Lime juice	$^{1}/_2$ tsp
Food colouring	A few drops

METHOD

- Place grated coconut in a piece of muslin and squeeze to extract No.1 coconut milk. Collect in a bowl. Measure 285 ml (1$^{1}/_4$ cups) of the No.1 milk for the batter and another 340 ml (1$^{1}/_2$ cups) of No.1 milk for the sauce. Set aside in separate bowls.
- Add 1.1 litres (4$^{3}/_4$ cups) water to the grated coconut and squeeze again to extract No.2 milk. Collect in a bowl.
- Measure 370 ml (1$^{2}/_3$ cups) of No.2 milk for the batter and another 730 ml (3$^{1}/_4$ cup) of No.2 milk for the sauce (*see Apom Sauce recipe on page 120*). Set aside in separate bowls.
- In a mixing bowl, combine yeast, plain flour, castor sugar and 5 Tbsp coconut water. Set aside for 4–6 minutes or until frothy.
- In a saucepan, heat the 285 ml (1$^{1}/_4$ cups) No.1 milk over low flame until it turns creamy. Do not let it boil over. Set aside.
- In another mixing bowl, combine rice flour, glutinous rice flour, salt and cold water. Add the 370 ml (1$^{2}/_3$ cups) No.2 milk, the yeast-and-flour mixture. Mix it with your hands until it becomes a smooth batter.

- Add in the 285 ml (1$^{1}/_4$ cups) coconut water and continue kneading briefly. Blend in the heated No.1 milk.
- Cover bowl and leave to stand in a warm place for 1–2 hours. Beat lightly with a wooden spoon every 10 minutes.
- To test if batter is ready, take a tablespoon of batter and place in a heated, slightly greased pan. Batter is ready if it bubbles and cooks, forming holes all over.
- Pour 140 ml (just over $^{1}/_2$ cup) of the batter into a cup, stir in the food colouring and lime juice. You will end up with a portion of coloured batter and uncoloured batter. Set both aside.

To fry the *apom*

- Heat *apom berkuah* pan (*see inset picture*) until very hot, remove and grease. Return pan over moderately high heat. Stir uncoloured batter and pour into all the patty pans. Quickly take $^{1}/_2$ tsp of the coloured batter and spread over the uncoloured batter in a circular motion before it starts to bubble. Reduce heat when the cake bubbles and forms tiny holes all over.
- Sprinkle over with a little water and cook covered for another 4–5 minutes.
- To remove, loosen cake from the pan with a knife and cool on a cake rack.

To serve

To serve in individual portions, place 2 or 3 pieces of *apom berkuah* on a plate and pour some sauce (*recipe on page 115*) and bananas over it.

Note:
Always grease the pan before you cook each batch of the batter. You can use flavoured oil to grease the patty pans to give the *kuih* added fragrance. Combine 225 ml (1 cup) cooking oil with 115 g (4 oz) grated coconut and 4 screwpine (*pandan*) leaves which have been cut into smaller pieces. Boil together until the coconut turns light brown. Strain and cool before use. If using dessicated coconut, dampen slightly before boiling. Store in refrigerator for future use.

Apom Sauce

INGREDIENTS

Bananas *(pisang raja)*	10
Rice flour	55 g (2 oz)
Plain flour	3 Tbsp
No.2 coconut milk*	220 ml (1 cup)
Palm sugar *(gula Melaka)*	225 g (8 oz), finely grated
Sugar	140 g (5 oz)
Water	115 ml (^{1}/$_2$ cup)
Screwpine *(pandan)* leaves	8, cut into short lengths
Salt	^{1}/$_4$ tsp
No.2 coconut milk*	510 ml (2^1/$_4$ cups)
No.1 coconut milk*	340 ml (1^1/$_2$ cups)

METHOD

- Steam bananas for 7 minutes. Leave to cool. Slice.
- In a bowl, combine rice flour, plain flour and the 225 ml (1 cup) No.2 coconut milk and blend until smooth. Set aside.
- In a saucepan, combine palm sugar, sugar, water, screwpine leaves and salt and bring to the boil for 5 minutes. Add 510 ml (2^1/$_4$ cups) of No.2 coconut milk and bring to the boil again. Strain into a heavy saucepan.
- Place saucepan over gentle heat and gradually add the flour mixture, stirring constantly. Boil gently, then add the 340 ml (1^1/$_2$ cups) No.1 coconut milk.
- Add in the bananas and cook until just boiling. (Do not over boil as the sauce will turn oily and lose its richness.)
- Transfer sauce to a large bowl, and stand it in a basin of cold water to cool.

Note:

*Coconut milk reserved from making the apom (*see page 119*)

Nasi Pulut with Seri Kaya

GLUTINOUS RICE CAKE WITH RICH EGG CUSTARD

Nasi Pulut

INGREDIENTS

Coconut	560 g (1¼ lb), skinned and grated
Water	170 ml (¾ cup)
Castor sugar	1 Tbsp
Salt	1½ tsp
Screwpine (*pandan*) leaves	8, knotted
Glutinous rice	600 g (21 oz)

METHOD

- Wash glutinous rice and soak for 4 hours. Drain.
- Place coconut in a piece of muslin and squeeze to extract No.1 milk. You should end up with about 225 ml (1 cup). Set aside.
- Add 170 ml (¾ cup) water to the grated coconut. Using the muslin, squeeze the coconut again to extract 170 ml (¾ cup) No.2 milk. Collect separately and set aside.
- Add the sugar and salt to the No.1 milk and stir until dissolved.
- Place the screwpine leaves and glutinous rice in a shallow bowl and steam over rapidly boiling water for 20 minutes. (Make steam holes in the rice before steaming.)
- Transfer glutinous rice to a saucepan and stir in the No.2 milk. Cover and set aside for 5 minutes.
- Return glutinous rice to the shallow bowl and steam for another 7 minutes. Transfer rice to a saucepan again and stir in No.1 milk. Cover and set aside for 5 minutes.
- Place rice in the bowl again and steam one last time for 7 minutes.
- Transfer to a large plate to cool. Cut the glutinous rice cake into squares and serve with *seri kaya* (*see recipe on page 122*).

Note:
To create a marbling effect, colour one-quarter of the steamed glutinous rice blue and add 1 Tbsp lime juice. Roughly mix with the uncoloured glutinous rice for a marbled effect.

Seri Kaya

INGREDIENTS

Coconut	900 g (2 lb), skinned and grated
Eggs	10
Sugar	560 g (1 1/4 lb)
Screwpine (*pandan*) leaves	2, knotted

METHOD

Stirring method

- Place grated coconut into a piece of muslin and squeeze to extract 340 ml (1 1/2 cups) No.1 milk. Collect in a bowl.
- Place eggs and sugar in another bowl and beat.
- Pour into a saucepan with screwpine leaves and heat over very low flame to dissolve the sugar – about 10 minutes. Stir often. Remove from the heat and discard the screwpine leaves.
- Add the No.1 milk to the egg mixture, then strain into an enamel dish.
- Place the dish with the egg mixture on a rack over a saucepan of rapidly boiling water.
- Stir the mixture constantly for 45 minutes until the egg mixture turns thick like custard cream.

Steaming method

- If you prefer to steam the *seri kaya*, prepare as above but strain the egg mixture into a heat-proof dish with a lid instead of a enamel dish. Wrap lid with a dry tea towel and cover the *kaya*.
- Steam, covered, for 3 hours over moderate heat. Do not stir.
- Dry the underside of the saucepan's lid occasionally to prevent the *seri kaya* from discolouring. Change tea towel if necessary.

Note:
Seri kaya **is best steamed over a charcoal burner.**

Kuih Lopis

GLUTINOUS RICE WITH COCONUT AND PALM SUGAR SYRUP

INGREDIENTS

Glutinous rice	455 g (1 lb)
Alkaline water	2 Tbsp (recipe on page 13)
Palm sugar (gula Melaka)	285 g (10 oz)
Sugar	2 Tbsp
Water	170 ml (³/4 cup)
Screwpine (pandan) leaves	5, sliced
Salt	A pinch
Coconut	455 g (1 lb), skinned and grated

Kuih Lopis can also be cooked in specially-made aluminium tubes (*see picture below*). The tubes can be purchased from shops selling cooking and baking equipement. Line the inside of the tube with banana leaf, fill with the rice three-quater full, cover and boil for 3 hours.

METHOD

- Wash glutinous rice until water runs clear.
- Place rice in a container and add enough water until water level is 5 cm (2 in) above level of rice. Add the alkaline water and soak for 4 hours.
- Rinse rice and drain. Set aside for 20 minutes.
- Make two cloth bags for the rice: Cut two pieces of white cloth to measure 30 cm x 20 cm (12 in x 8 in). Fold the material into halves lengthwise and sew it shut 0.5 cm from the edge.
- Use a string to tie one open end of the bag 5 cm away from the edge. Divide rice into 2 parts. Fill each bag with one part. Pack the rice firmly and tie the bag to resemble a cylinder. Repeat process with the other bag.
- Place a low steaming rack into a saucepan of boiling water, and boil the bags of rice over constant high heat for 3 hours. The bags should always be completely immersed in the water.
- Remove bags from saucepan and let cool overnight. Untie bags and cut *kuih lopis* into thick slices.
- Prepare the syrup: Grate the palm sugar, add sugar, water, screwpine leaves and boil in a saucepan for 10 minutes until syrup is fairly thick. Set aside.
- To serve: Mix the salt evenly with the grated coconut. For each serving, put 2 slices of *kuih lopis* on a plate and top with 2 Tbsp of grated coconut and some syrup.

Note:
Remove the transparent glutinous rice grains from the chalky white glutinous rice grains before making *kuih lopis*.

Dampen the bags of cooked glutinous rice and leave for 10–15 minutes before removing the rice. This will allow the cloth bags to slide off easily from the lopis.

Onde-Onde

INGREDIENTS

Screwpine (*pandan*) leaves	10
Water	1 Tbsp
Glutinous rice flour	225 g (8 oz)
Tapioca flour or cornflour	55 g (2 oz)
Salt	A pinch
Castor sugar	2 tsp
Water	140 ml (^{1}/$_2$ cup and 2 Tbsp)
Cooking oil	1 Tbsp
Green food colouring	A few drops
Coconut	85 g (10 oz), skinned, grated, mixed with a pinch of salt
Palm sugar (*gula Melaka*)	170 g (6 oz), finely grated and mixed with 1 Tbsp castor sugar

METHOD

- Cut screwpine leaves into small pieces and pound until very fine.
- Add 1 Tbsp water to the pounded leaves. Using a piece of muslin, squeeze the screwpine leaf paste to extract juice. Set aside.
- In a large mixing bowl, combine glutinous rice flour, tapioca or cornflour, salt and castor sugar.
- Place the 140 ml (^{1}/$_2$ cup and 2 Tbsp) water in a saucepan and bring to a boil. Add the cooking oil and green food colouring. Pour onto the flour mixture and stir.
- Add the screwpine juice to the flour mixture and knead to form a smooth dough.
- Divide dough into 4 equal portions and roll each of them into thin logs. Divide each log into nine pieces.
- Cover dough with a damp cloth to prevent dough from drying up.
- Bring a saucepan of water to a boil.
- Spread the grated coconut on a tray.
- Grease the palms of your hand, then take a piece of dough and roll into a ball. Make an indentation in the dough ball and fill with a teaspoon of grated palm sugar.
- Seal the filling completely with the dough and smoothen the seam in the dough. (*Note*: If it is not well sealed, the sugar will ooze out whilst boiling.)
- Place the *onde-onde* balls into the saucepan of boiling water and boil until they float to the surface.
- Scoop out with a wire mesh ladle and roll it in the grated coconut to coat. Repeat with the rest. Serve.

Kuih Khoo

STEAMED RICE CAKE WITH GREEN BEAN FILLING

INGREDIENTS

Sweet potatoes	115 g (4 oz), skinned and chopped
Glutinous rice flour	455 g (1 lb)
Coconut	680 g (1^1/$_2$ lb), skinned and grated
Sugar	2 Tbsp
Cooking oil	2 Tbsp
Salt	^{1}/$_2$ tsp
Red food colouring	A few drops
Banana leaves	20, trimmed to fit mould

METHOD

- Place sweet potatoes in a saucepan, add water to cover and bring to a gentle boil. Cook until tender, then mash while still hot.
- In a large mixing bowl, combine the mashed sweet potatoes with 285 g (10 oz) of the glutinous rice flour. Set aside.
- Using a piece of muslin, squeeze grated coconut to extract No.1 milk. Set aside 285 ml (1^1/$_4$ cups) of the coconut milk in a bowl. Add 170 ml (^{3}/$_4$ cup) water to the grated coconut and squeeze again to extract 170 ml (^{3}/$_4$ cup) of No.2 milk. Collect in a separate bowl.
- Add sugar, cooking oil and salt to the No.2 milk.
- Boil No.2 milk mixture in a saucepan, then add a few drops of red food colouring. Remove from heat, then add in the remaining glutinous rice flour.
- Add the hot rice flour mixture to the sweet potato mixture. Pour in the No.1 milk gradually and mix to form a dough.
- Place dough on a board lightly dusted with glutinous rice flour. Knead to form a smooth dough. Set aside in a bowl and cover with a damp cloth until ready for filling.

To mould *kuih khoo*

- Pour 115 ml (^{1}/$_2$ cup) corn oil into a bowl. Oil hands and divide dough into 20 equal parts.
- Roll each dough portion into a ball. Make an indentation in each ball and place a piece of bean filling (*see recipe on page 130*) in it. Gather up the edges of the dough and pinch together to cover the filling completely.
- Oil palms of hands again and shape the filled dough into a ball. Place each dough ball in the middle of the *kuih khoo* mould (*see picture below*) and press firmly until it fills the mould and obtains a deep impression of the pattern.
- Turn out each cake on to a piece of banana leaf. Repeat process with the rest of the dough. These cakes are ready for steaming (*see how to steam the cakes on page 130*).

Note:
Cut each piece of banana leaf according to the size of the mould used. The leaves will shrink during steaming, so leave a 2-cm (^{1}/$_2$-in) allowance around the edge of the leaf. Trim neatly when the cake is cool.

Colouring: The cakes will turn a deeper red after steaming, so do not add too much colouring to the dough. Mix with a little hot water before adding to the dough.

To Steam *Kuih Khoo*

METHOD

- Arrange *kuih khoo* in a steamer tray and steam over medium heat for 7–10 minutes. The water in the steamer must be boiling gently, or cakes will not retain its pattern. Wipe the inside lid of the steamer occasionally.
- When done, transfer cakes to a rack and brush lightly with cooking oil while still hot.
- When cakes are cool, trim the banana leaves to neatly fit the base of each cake. Arrange cakes on a tray, overlapping one another. Cover with a big piece of banana leaf until ready to serve. This will keep the cakes soft and moist.

Note:
Storage: When cakes are cool, store them in a plastic container to keep them soft. Exposure to cold air will harden the cakes.

Bean Filling

INGREDIENTS

Green beans	560 g (1 1/4 lb), washed, soaked overnight, skinned and drained
Water	140 ml (2/3 cup)
Screwpine (*pandan*) leaves	8, knotted
Sugar	620 g (1 lb 6 oz)

METHOD

- Steam green beans until soft, about 20 minutes. Mash the beans while hot, then set aside.
- Boil the water in a wok. Add the screwpine leaves and sugar and boil over a low heat until it turns syrupy.
- Add the mashed beans and continue cooking until almost dry, stirring constantly. Discard the screwpine leaves and let the mixture cool.
- Roll the bean mixture into 20 small balls and place them on a tray until ready for filling.

Pulut Panggang

GRILLED GLUTINOUS RICE DUMPLINGS WITH DRIED PRAWNS

INGREDIENTS

Banana leaves	35–40, measuring 12 cm x l6 cm (5 in x 6 in)
Coconut	570 g (1 1/4 lb), skinned and grated
Salt	2 tsp
Castor sugar	1 1/2 Tbsp
Glutinous rice	900 g (2 lb), washed and soaked overnight
Screwpine (*pandan*) leaves	8, knotted

METHOD

- Scald banana leaves in boiling water for 2 minutes. Allow to soak for another 2 minutes, then wipe dry.
- Place grated coconut in a piece of muslin and squeeze to extract 225 ml (1 cup) No.1 milk. Collect in a bowl. Stir in the salt and sugar and set aside.
- Add 225 ml (1 cup) water to the grated coconut and squeeze again for No.2 milk. Collect in a separate bowl and set aside.
- Place glutinous rice and screwpine leaves in a dish, make steam holes in the rice and steam over rapidly boiling water for 20 minutes.
- Transfer glutinous rice to a saucepan, mix in the No.2 milk and cover for 5 minutes.
- Return rice to the dish, make steam holes and steam again for 7 minutes. Place rice in saucepan and blend in No.1 milk. Cover for 5 minutes then steam for a further 5 minutes. Turn off the heat, but leave glutinous rice in the steamer. Cover with kitchen towel.

To assemble *pulut panggang*

- Wet hands. Take a small handful of the warm glutinous rice and squeeze lightly to form a firm oval shape.
- Use index finger and tunnel along the length of the glutinous rice. Fill the tunnel with the filling (*see recipe on page 132*), ensuring that the filling sits in the centre.
- Seal both edges to form a cylindrical shape and wrap with banana leaf. Staple both ends of the leaf. Repeat with the rest of the glutinous rice.
- When it is all wrapped, heat a grill until very hot. Place the glutinous rice cakes 5 cm (2 in) below the grill and grill for 7–8 minutes to brown all sides. (Alternatively, grill over charcoal fire on a satay burner.)

Note:
A combination of blue and white glutinous rice can be used. To colour, mix one-third of the steamed glutinous rice with a few drops of blue food colouring and 1 tsp lime juice. Mix the blue glutinous rice with the white to create a marbling effect.

Filling for Pulut Panggang

INGREDIENTS

Shallots or onions	55 g (2 oz), peeled
Candlenuts	8
Lemon grass	1 stalk, thinly sliced
Water	55 ml ($^1/_4$ cup)
Cornflour	1 Tbsp
Dark soy sauce	2 tsp
Coconut	170 g (6 oz), grated
Dried prawns	85 g (3 oz), finely pounded
Cooking oil	8 Tbsp
Sugar	4 Tbsp
Pepper	2 tsp
Coriander seeds	1 Tbsp, roasted and ground

METHOD

- Combine shallots or onions, candlenuts and lemon grass and pound to a fine paste. Set aside.
- In a small bowl, combine the water, cornflour and dark soy sauce and set aside. (Stir again just before use.)
- Place grated coconut in a heated wok and fry over low heat until light brown.
- Add the dried prawns and continue frying for a further 20 minutes. Transfer to a plate.
- Place cooking oil in a saucepan and heat until hot. Add the pounded shallot mixture and fry until fragrant and light brown.
- Add the sugar, pepper and coriander and stir. Then add the fried coconut, dried prawns and the cornflour solution and mix well to blend.
- Transfer to a plate to cool.

Red Beans with Coconut Créme

INGREDIENTS

Water	1.5 litres (6³/₄ cups)
Red beans	285 g (10 oz), washed and drained
Dried orange peel	¹/₂–³/₄ piece, thinly sliced, optional
Screwpine (*pandan*) leaves	6, knotted, optional
Sugar	250 g (9 oz)
Lotus seed in syrup	1 can (455 ml)

METHOD

- In a saucepan, combine water, red beans, orange peel, if using, and screwpine leaves, if using, and boil until red beans are soft.
- Leave to cool for 15 minutes and discard screwpine leaves. Place batches of the red bean into a blender and blend until smooth.
- Return the blended beans into the saucepan, add sugar and boil again. Add lotus seeds and boil gently for 10 minutes.
- Pour red bean soup into a large serving bowl, add coconut créme (*see recipe below*) and serve hot.

Coconut Créme

INGREDIENTS

Instant coconut powder	30 g (1 oz) (SANTAN brand instant coconut powder recommended)
Water	350 ml (1¹/₂ cups)
Plain flour	1 Tbsp
Salt	¹/₂ tsp
Sugar	1 tsp
Screwpine (*pandan*) leaves	3, knotted, optional

METHOD

- In a bowl, combine coconut powder, water, plain flour, salt and sugar and strain into a saucepan.
- Add screwpine leaves, if using, and bring to a boil over moderate heat. Stir often to prevent lumps from forming.
- Cool completely and chill in refrigerator until ready to serve.

Bubur Cha-Cha

YAM TREAT

INGREDIENTS

Coconut	900 g (2 lb), skinned and grated
Sweet potatoes	300 g (11 oz), skinned and diced
Yam	300 g (11 oz), skinned and diced
Salt	1/2–1 tsp

Syrup

Water	225 ml (1 cup)
Screwpine (*pandan*) leaves	6, knotted
Sugar	140 g (5 oz)

Sago Flour Triangles

Sago flour	300 g (11 oz)
Borax (*tingkal*)	1/2 tsp (*available from Chinese dispensaries*)
Boiling water	225 ml (1 cup)
Red, green and blue food colouring	A few drops
Sugar	4 Tbsp

METHOD

- Place coconut in a piece of muslin and squeeze to extract No.1 milk. Collect in a bowl.
- Add 560 ml (2 1/2 cups) water to the grated coconut and squeeze again for No.2 milk. Collect in a separate bowl.
- Rinse and drain sweet potatoes and steam for 5–7 minutes until cooked. Set aside.
- Steam yam cubes for 5–7 minutes till cooked. Set aside.
- Make the syrup: Bring the 225 ml (1 cup) water to a boil. Add the screwpine leaves and sugar and boil for 10 minutes. Strain syrup into a bowl and set aside.

To make sago flour triangles

- Sift together sago flour and borax. Then stir in the boiling water.
- Using your hands, knead to form a firm, smooth dough.
- Divide dough into four parts. Leave one part uncoloured, and colour the other three portions. Knead them separately to work in the colour.
- Roll each part into thin long strips of about 1 cm in diameter. Use a pair of scissors, cut each strip into small triangles.
- Bring a saucepan of water to a boil. Place the sago triangles in the boiling water, stirring to keep them from sticking. When they float, scoop them out quickly and plunge into a basin of cold water for 10 minutes.
- Drain and place flour triangles in a bowl. Add 4 Tbsp sugar and mix to keep the cooked sago triangles separated.

To prepare the coconut milk

- In a saucepan, combine the syrup and No.2 coconut milk and bring to a boil over low heat, stirring constantly.
- Pour in the No.1 milk, add salt and stir well. Remove from the heat and keep stirring for a while to prevent the mixture from curdling and turning oily.

To serve

Place a tablespoonful each of cooked sweet potatoes, yam and sago triangles in a small bowl. Add coconut milk to fill the bowl. Serve hot or cold.

Note:
When cooking large amounts of coconut milk, place the saucepan of boiled coconut milk in a large basin of cold water and stir to cool and prevent curdling.

Clean yam with a brush. Wipe it dry and remove the dark skin. Do not wash after removing the skin or it will be slimey. Keep diced yam dry.

Cendol

COCONUT MILK GRANITA

INGREDIENTS

Screwpine (*pandan*) leaves	10, finely pounded
Water	1.2 litres (5 1/3 cups)
Salt	1/4 tsp
Green food colouring	1 tsp
Green pea flour	1 packet, 'Flower' brand

METHOD

To prepare green pea droplets

- Prepare a basin of iced water.
- Mix the pounded screwpine leaves with the 1.2 litres (5 1/3 cups) water. Squeeze and strain liquid. Add the salt and food colouring and set aside.
- In a bowl, blend 225 ml (1 cup) of the screwpine liquid with the green pea flour. Set aside.
- Place the remaining screwpine liquid in a saucepan and boil. Remove from the heat and slowly stir in the green pea flour mixture.
- Return the saucepan to the stove and cook over low heat, stirring constantly until it boils.
- Remove from the heat immediately when it boils. Leave to stand for 5 minutes.
- Place the frame for making green pea flour droplets (*see inset picture*) over the basin of iced water. Pour the hot green pea flour mixture on to the frame. Using a flat spatula, press mixture in long, downward strokes. The flour mixture will fall through the holes in droplets into the iced water below.
- Leave droplets to set in the iced water until firm. If necessary, add more ice to the water to help the flour drops set faster.
- Drain, then chill in the refrigerator until ready to serve.

To assemble *cendol*

Spoon green pea flour droplets into glasses, add some crushed ice and pour coconut milk (*see recipe below*) to fill glasses. Serve with palm sugar syrup (*see recipe below*) according to taste. Add salt if necessary.

Note:
This recipe makes between 1 litre and 1.2 litres (4 1/2 cups–5 1/3 cups) of *cendol*, or 20–30 servings. Green pea droplets can also be bought ready made from supermarkets.

Palm Sugar Syrup

INGREDIENTS

Palm sugar (*gula Melaka*)	625 g (1 lb 6 oz), grated
Sugar	6 Tbsp
Water	225 ml (1 cup)
Screwpine (*pandan*) leaves	6, knotted

METHOD

- Combine all the syrup ingredients and boil for 1/2 hour.
- Strain and set aside until ready to serve.

Coconut Milk

INGREDIENTS

Coconut	2 kg (4 1/2 lb), skinned and grated
Water	900 ml (4 cups)
Salt	1–1 1/2 tsp

METHOD

- Combine water and coconut. Place handfuls of the mixture in a piece of muslin and squeeze to extract coconut milk. Collect in a bowl.
- Add salt and chill in refrigerator until ready to serve.

Goreng Pisang

DEEP-FRIED BANANAS

INGREDIENTS

Salt	1 tsp
Lime paste	1 tsp *(see note below)*
Lime or lemon juice	1 Tbsp
Water	115 ml (¹/₂ cup)
Wet rice flour	285 g (10 oz) *(recipe on page 13)*
Cooking oil for deep-frying	
Bananas *(pisang raja)*	12–14, skinned
Plain flour for dusting	

METHOD

- In a bowl, combine salt, lime paste, lime or lemon juice and water.
- Place wet rice flour in a mixing bowl. Add the lime mixture to the flour and blend until the batter is smooth and coats the back of a spoon.
- Let batter stand for ¹/₂ hour.
- Place cooking oil in a pan and heat until very hot.
- Place bananas on a tray and dust lightly with plain flour.
- Dip the bananas in the batter and very quickly put them into the hot oil. Deep-fry until golden brown, stirring occasionally.
- Remove and place on kitchen towels to soak up the excess oil.
- Serve hot.

Note:
Lime paste refers to the white chalky edible lime that is used for betelnut chewing. It can be bought at any Indian grocer or specialty baking shop.

Do not use over-ripe bananas. Fry as many as bananas as you wish at a time, but make sure the oil in the pan completely covers the bananas.

Kuih Kuria

TAPIOCA DOUGHNUTS

INGREDIENTS

Tapioca	455 g (1 lb), skinned and grated with centre vein removed
Coconut	170 g (6 oz), skinned and grated
Glutinous rice flour or sago flour	3 Tbsp
Salt	$^3/_4$ tsp
Cooking oil for deep-frying	
Water	55 ml ($^1/_4$ cup)
Sugar	225 g (8 oz)
Screwpine (*pandan*) leaves	4, knotted

METHOD

- In a bowl, combine tapioca, coconut, glutinous rice flour and salt.
- Form tapioca mixture into small balls, flatten and make a hole in the centre just like American doughnuts. Alternatively, roll out tapioca mixture into 1.5-cm ($^3/_4$-in) thickness. Cut with doughnut cutter (*see picture on the left below*).
- Heat cooking oil in a wok and deep-fry tapioca rings until golden brown. Remove and drain on absorbent paper.
- Drain oil from wok. Do not wash. Add the water, sugar and screwpine leaves. Place over heat and bring to a boil until sugar is caramelized and syrupy.
- Reduce heat to very low and return the doughnuts to the wok. Stir rings to coat with the syrup. Remove wok from heat but keep tossing the doughnuts in the wok until the sugar is dry.
- Leave to cool on a rack. Serve.

Bubur Terigu

INGREDIENTS

Sugar	115 g (4 oz)
Palm sugar (*gula Melaka*)	285 g (10 oz)
Screwpine (*pandan*) leaves	8
Water	225 ml (1 cup)
Quick cooking oats	55 g (2 oz)
Water	285 ml (1 1/4 cups)
Coconut	680 g (1 1/2 lb), skinned and grated
Salt	1/4 tsp
Water	285 ml (1 1/4 cups)
Wheat (*biji terigu*)	285 g (10 oz), husk removed
Water	1.7 litres (7 1/2 cups)
Plain flour	3 Tbsp, mixed with 170 ml (3/4 cup) water to be used as thickening

METHOD

- In a pan, combine sugars, screwpine leaves and the 225 ml (1 cup) water and boil for 10 minutes. Strain and set aside.
- In another pan, combine oats and the 285 ml (1 1/4 cups) water. Bring to a boil and cook for 5–7 minutes. Set aside.
- Using a piece of muslin, squeeze grated coconut to extract 400 ml (1 3/4 cups) of No.1 milk. Collect in a bowl, stir in the salt and set aside.
- Add the 285 ml (1 1/4 cups) water to grated coconut and squeeze again to extract No.2 milk. Collect separately and set aside.
- Soak wheat in a bowl of cold water for 10 minutes, then drain.
- Pound small amounts of wheat gently using pestle to break up the wheat. Place it in a pot with 1.7 litres (7 1/2 cups) water and boil for 45 minutes, or until the wheat is swollen and tender. Reduce heat.
- Gradually pour in the sugar syrup, oat mixture and flour solution, stirring often.
- Finally, add the No.2 milk and boil for 2 minutes. Remove from heat.
- To serve: Pour *bubur terigu* in individual bowls and top with 2 Tbsp of No.1 milk. Serve hot.

glossaryofingredients

NYONYA SPECIALTIES – THE BEST OF SINGAPORE'S RECIPES

SPICES

1. Aniseed
Similar in flavour as star anise, aniseed is popular in Chinese cooking, adding a delicate licorice taste to sweet and savoury dishes. It is available whole, as tiny egg-shaped seeds or in powdered form and can be bought in health food stores, Chinese delicatessens and some large supermarkets. It is also used in baking, especially biscuits and cakes, in preserving, such as plums and gherkins, in anise-flavoured liqueurs and drinks, and to mask the strong flavours of some cough medicines.

2. Cardamom
Cardamom is the world's most expensive spice after saffron. Cardamom pods are the dried fruits of a perennial plant of the ginger family indigenous to Sri Lanka and south India. The pale green oval pods, which are the best variety, contain 15–20 brown or black seeds. The white pods are simply green pods that have been bleached in the sun.

3, 4, 5. Chilli
Native to Mexico, chillies are now available in many forms – fresh, dried, powdered, flaked as well in the form of sauces, *sambal* and pastes. They range from mild to wild, and the smaller the chilli, the hotter it is, e.g. bird's eye chillies.

Chillies are used either unripe, when they are green, or ripe, after they turn red. Ripe chillies are hotter then green ones. Red chillies are usually pounded or ground into a paste, chopped or used whole for flavouring, or cut in different ways for garnishing. Green chillies are generally used whole for flavouring, or cut in different ways for garnishing. Both red and green chillies are also available pickled. Dried chillies are pounded or ground and used for flavouring and seasoning.

Related to cayenne and Tabasco chillies, the colour of bird's eye chillies may range from deep red to cream, yellow or orange. Thin-fleshed with a deep fiery heat, its flavour may range from mild to sweet.

6. Cinnamon
Cinnamon, the edible bark of the tree native to Sri Lanka, is probably the most popular cooking spice in the Western world. The innermost layer of the bark is sold as thin, fragile quills in India, Sri Lanka, Indonesia and Malaysia and Singapore and is used for flavouring meat, poultry and desserts. The spice is also available powdered, but its flavour and aroma dissipate rather quickly in this form.

7. Clove
Cloves are actually the flower buds of a tree of the myrtle family indigenous to the Maluku Island (Moluccas) or the Spice Islands. The buds are harvested and dried under the sun for days. Cloves have a stronger flavour than most other spices and are therefore used in smaller quantities.

8. Coriander seeds
With their clean, lemony flavour, coriander seeds are a major component of most curry powder used in India, Sri Lanka, Indonesia, Malaysia and other countries. Freshly ground coriander is more fragrant than coriander that is purchased already powdered.

9. Cumin
Cumin is used in Middle Eastern, Asian and Mediterranean cooking. This aromatic spice has a nutty flavour and is available whole or ground. It is popularly used to flavour curries, stews and Indian yoghurt drinks (*lassi*).

10. Fenugreek
The seeds and tender sprouted leaves of fenugreek, native to Europe and Asia, are both edible. The seeds, with their bitter flavour, are an important component of Indian curry powders. The seeds are also used whole in some Sri Lankan and Malaysian dishes, particularly seafood curries.

11. Five-spice powder
Frequently used in all sorts of Chinese dishes, it summons up the taste and smell of China. As the name implies, it is made up of five ground spices – Szechuan pepper, cinnamon, clove, fennel seeds and star anise.

Available from delicatessens, Chinese markets and some health food shops, it should be kept in a sealed container in a dry place. Like most spices, it will keep for several months but will gradually lose its fragrance and flavour and therefore should not be kept for too long.

12. Galangal
Greater galangal is native to Malaysia and Java. It has a delicate flavour and is used fresh in Malaysian, Indonesian and Thai cooking. When the fresh variety is not available, dried and powdered galangal can be used instead.

The young rhizome is pale pink and is more tender and flavourful than the mature one, which is beige in colour. Galangal belongs to the ginger family but cannot be used as a substitute for the common ginger, as its pungency and tang is distinctively different. It is added to curries or dishes in slices, chunks or as a paste. As it is quite fibrous, chop it into small pieces before pounding or grinding it.

13. Garlic
Garlic is used with almost anything, except maybe dessert. Its flavour depends on how it is prepared – cooked garlic being much milder than raw, chopped garlic. It can be used raw or fried, poached, roasted or sautéed, and can be cooked peeled or unpeeled. Choose a firm, hard head of garlic with no soft or discoloured patches. Do not refrigerate but store in a cool, dry place.

14. Ginger
Ginger, a fleshy rhizome, is used in the West to make gingerbread, ginger beer, candied ginger and chocolate ginger. Fresh ginger is a basic ingredient in many Asian cuisines. It is usually sliced, finely chopped, pounded or ground and used in savoury dishes. Sometimes the juice is extracted and used.

15. Nutmeg
Buy whole and grate as needed. Nutmeg is used to flavour soups, vegetables, breads and cakes. A true Bolognese sauce is not complete without grated nutmeg.

16. Onion
Onions are indispensable in our day-to-day cooking. There are dry onions and green onions. Dry onions are left in the ground to mature and have a tougher, outer skin for longer storage. Green onions are merely young and immature. There are many varieties and many ways to use them.

17. Oom (ajowan) seeds
Also called omum seed, carom seed or Bishop's weed, this is the small seed of a herb belonging to the cumin and parsley family, and has the flavour of thyme. It is used sparingly in Indian lentil dishes and pickles due to its strong flavour.

18, 19. Pepper

Peppers are small, round berries that grow in trailing clusters. They start off a deep green and turn red as they ripen. Black pepper is obtained by drying the green berries in the sun, which makes the outer skin black and shrivelled.

White pepper is obtained by packing the ripe berries in sacks, soaking them in slow-flowing water for eight days and then rubbing off the softened outer skin. The inner portion is then dried in the sun for several days until it turns a creamy white. White pepper is hotter than black pepper, but it is not as fragrant.

20. Shallot

A small bulb with a sweeter, lighter, more delicate flavour than an onion. There are a number of varieties including grey, pink and brown. Most easily obtained in spring and summer, shallots are often required in dishes from France.

21. Star anise

Star anise comes from a tree belonging to the magnolia family. The dried eight-pointed star-shaped pod is used for flavouring meat and poultry dishes in Malaysia, Singapore, Indonesia, China and Vietnam.

22. Turmeric

This yellow coloured rhizome is related to ginger and used in many dishes in India. It is also added to Thai curries. The fresh root has an aromatic and spicy fragrance which can be lost by drying. Turmeric is available fresh or powdered. In a recipe, 1 Tbsp chopped turmeric is equivalent to $^1/_4$ tsp powdered turmeric.

VEGETABLES

23. Bamboo shoots

These are the young shoots of the bamboo. Fresh bamboo shoots must be boiled for at least 1 hour to soften before they can be used. After boiling, soak them in water until required. Boiled and ready-to-use bamboo shoots are available in packets or canned from Chinese grocery stores and some supermarkets.

24. Bean sprouts

In Asia, bean sprouts are grown from either mung beans (green beans) or soy beans, while in the west they are always grown from mung beans. If the sprouts are to be eaten raw, use mung bean sprouts. Soy bean sprouts have to be cooked for 10 minutes before they can be eaten.

25. Bilimbi

This small fruit, locally known as *belimbing asam* or *belimbing buluh*, is light green or yellow in colour and resembles a tiny cucumber. It has a sour taste. Fresh bilimbi is added to dishes such as *sambal* and curries to tenderise the meat and to give a tangy flavour. This versatile fruit can be pickled or preserved with salt and then dried and used as a substitute for tamarind (*asam*).

26. Bittergourd

This wrinkled, cucumber-like vegetable is eaten while still unripe. With bitter tasting flesh which improves when cooked, the bittergourd features in Southeast Asian dishes such as cooked salads and stir-fries. It is also made into a tart pickle and is popular in India. According to Asian kitchen wisdom, the more grooves on the bittergourd, the more bitter it will be.

27. Brinjal

This vegetable comes in two varieties – egg-shape and long. They are either white or deep purple. The purple variety has a thicker skin, but there is no difference in flavour. They are also called aubergines.

28. Cabbage

Cabbage is related to broccoli, cauliflower, kohlrabi and Brussels sprouts. Choose heads which are heavy with crisp, shiny outer leaves. Eat raw in salads. Cook only for a minimum time in a covered saucepan and drain very well.

29. Carrot

Choose bright orange, shiny specimens; avoid those with soft spots or cracks or those which are limp. In spring, look for baby carrots with their green tops intact. Serve cooked or raw in salads.

30. Chinese mustard, preserved

This is the most commonly used preserved vegetable in Chinese cooking. This is Chinese mustard or leaf mustard that has been preserved in vinegar (*kiam chye*) and can keep indefinitely. It is used in stir fries and soups.

31. Cucumber

Although cucumbers are usually thought of as essential for salads and with crudités, it is also surprisingly good when braised and served as a vegetable, especially with fish and seafood dishes. Look for glossy, crisp, bright green vegetables.

32. Flowering cabbage

Flowering cabbage (*choy sum*) has green leaves, pale green stems and small yellow flowers. This vegetable can be steamed, stir-fried or blanched and used in noodle dishes, soup, etc.

33. French beans

This name encompasses a range of green beans, including the snap bean and the bobby bean. They are mostly fat and fleshy and when fresh, should be firm so that they break in half with a satisfying snapping sound.

34. Jackfruit

The jackfruit tree, native to India's Western Ghats, bears the world's largest fruit. The fruit is eaten both young and ripe. Green, with thick, sharp pines, the starchy young jackfruit is usually cooked as a vegetable. It is a staple source of starch in many Asian and South Pacific countries where it is fried, roasted or boiled. When ripe, it is eaten as a fruit or used in some Asian desserts.

35. Jicama

Originating from America, jicama (*bangkuang* or yam bean), locally referred to as 'Chinese turnip', are now cultivated in most countries in Asia. It has one root and is sweet, juicy and crunchy. It is an important ingredient in spring rolls or *poh pia*.

36. Lady's finger

Also called okra, this vegetable belongs to the hibiscus family. It is particularly popular in Creole and Cajun cooking. It has a glutinous texture and is a natural thickener. Soaking it for 30 minutes in vinegar, diluted with water, can minimize the viscosity.

37. Long beans

Also known as the Chinese bean, this very long, narrow, dark green variety is cooked as you would green beans.

38. Papaya
Indigenous to Central America, papayas range in size from very small to very large, and are eaten both ripe and green. When ripe, the papaya has soft juicy flesh and a fairly sweet taste (similar to apricot); it makes a good dessert or breakfast fruit. The unripe fruit, which has crisp, firm, tangy flesh, can be cooked as a vegetable, made into salads or used to make preserves and pickles. The fruit is very popular in Asia, where the flowers, leaves and young stem of the papaya tree are also cooked and eaten.

39. Pineapple
Native to South America, the pineapple is really a cluster of fruits of the Ananas tree that combine to form one 'multiple fruit'. The pineapple is one of the most popular tropical fruits. Available all year round, it makes an excellent dessert fruit. It can be bought fresh or canned. The fruit is delicious eaten ripe. In Asia, semi-ripe pineapple is used in sour soups and curries.

40. Pisang raja
These uniformly-shaped bananas are long and slim. When ripe, the skin is pale yellow and has a sweet fragrance. These bananas are popularly used in *goreng pisang*, where they are coated in batter and deep-fried as a tasty snack.

41. Potato
Originates from South America, potatoes are an important source of carbohydrates. Once thought to be fattening, potatoes can be part of a calorie-controlled diet. They are low in sodium, high in potassium and an important source of complex carbohydrates and vitamins C and B-6, as well as a storehouse of minerals.

Potatoes are available year-round. Choose potatoes that are suitable for the desired method of cooking. All potatoes should be firm, well-shaped (for their type) and blemish-free. New potatoes may be missing some of their feathery skin but other types should not have any bald spots. Avoid potatoes that are wrinkled, sprouted or cracked. Store potatoes in a cool, dark, well-ventilated place for up to 2 weeks. Warm temperatures encourage sprouting and shriveling.

42. Sugarcane
This is a tall Southeast Asian grass which has stout, fibrous, jointed stalks. These juicy canes produce sap which is a source of molasses and commercial sugar. In this part of the world, sugarcane is often squeezed to extract its juice and is drunk ice cold; cut into short lengths and chewed for its juice or boiled with water chestnuts to make a traditional Chinese tea.

43. Sweet potato
This elongated tuber comes in orange, white, yellow and purple. It is commonly used to make Asian desserts and is also added to salads to replace the potato. Prepare and cook as you would potatoes.

44. Tapioca
Tapioca in its fresh form is called yucca, which is another name for the root of the cassava plant. This root is also known as manioc or mandioca. When raw, it has a bland and sticky quality and is used in cooking the way you would a potato. It can be boiled, mashed or fried.

45. Tomato
Native to South America, dozens of tomato varieties are available today — ranging widely in size, shape and colour. Among the most commonly marketed are the beefsteak tomato, globe tomato, plum tomato and the small cherry tomato.

Choose firm, well-shaped tomatoes that are noticeably fragrant and richly coloured. They should be free from blemishes, heavy for their size and give slightly to palm pressure. Ripe tomatoes should be stored at room temperature and used within a few days. They should never be refrigerated — cold temperatures make the flesh pulpy and kills the flavour. Unripe fruit can be ripened by placing it in a pierced paper bag with an apple for several days at room temperature but do not refrigerate or set in the sun.

Tomatoes are rich in vitamin C and contain amounts of vitamins A and B, potassium, iron and phosphorus.

46. Water convolvulus
A green leafy vegetable, water convolvulus can be found growing wild beside streams. Some varieties have purple stems. If unavailable, substitute with spinach or watercress.

47. White radish
Also called daikon or mooli, it looks rather like a large white carrot, hence its Chinese name which literally means 'white carrot'. With a mild flavour and an ability to soak up other flavours, it is excellent for braising or used in delicate Chinese soups. It is also pickled.

HERBS

48. Basil leaf
Asian basil, also known as sweet basil, is widely used in Thailand. Several varieties are used to flavour foods. The sweet, aromatic fragrance of *bai horapa* graces many dishes while *maenglak*, or lemon basil, is used in soups. Basil leaves are best used fresh as they do not retain their flavour when dried.

49. Chinese celery
Similar in appearance to continental parsley, this is a stronger flavoured version of the more familiar celery. The colour may vary from white to dark green. Use in soups, stir-fries and stews.

50. Chinese chives
Also known as garlic chives, Chinese chives have thick, long flat leaves like the spring onion (scallion) and a stronger flavour than the Western chives. It is used both as a herb and vegetable in Southeast Asian cooking.

51. Chinese parsley
Also known as coriander leaves or cilantro, Chinese parsley is indigenous to southern Europe. All parts of the plant can be used, even the roots, which are an essential ingredient in Thai cooking. This herb is used to flavour and garnish dishes.

52. Curry leaves
Sprigs of small, shiny pointed leaves with a distinctive fragrance, curry leaves are used most frequently in south India , Sri Lanka, Malaysia and Singapore and Fiji. Fresh curry leaves are normally sautéed with onions while making curry. Dried curry leaves, which are probably easier to find in Western countries, are not as strongly flavoured, but they serve the purpose.

35 36 37 38 39 40 41 42 43 44 45 46 47 48 49 50 51

53. Kaffir lime leaves

These are the leaves from the kaffir lime plant. The lime is a small dark green citrus fruit with a thick, wrinkled and bumpy rind. Its leaves are easily recognised by its two distinct sections. The leaves are available fresh or dried, and are used in soups, curries and stir-fries.

54. Lemon grass

Lemon grass, a long lemon-scented grass, is popular for flavouring curries and soups in Malaysia and Singapore, Indonesia, Thailand and other Southeast Asian countries. Only the pale lower portion of the stem, with the tough outer layers peeled away, is used for cooking. If lemon grass is not available, two or three strips of thinly peeled lemon zest can be used as a substitute.

55. Mint leaves

There are over 30 species of mint, the two most popular and widely available being peppermint and spearmint. Peppermint is the more pungent of the two. It has bright green leaves, purple-tinged stems and a peppery flavour. Spearmint leaves are gray-green or true green and have a milder flavour and fragrance. Mint grows wild throughout the world and is cultivated in Europe, the United States and Asia. It's most plentiful during summer months but many markets carry it year-round.

Choose leaves that are evenly coloured with no sign of wilting. Store a bunch of mint, stems down, in a glass of water with a plastic bag over the leaves. Refrigerate in this manner for up to a week, changing the water every 2 days. Mint is available fresh, dried, as an extract and in the form of oil of spearmint or oil of peppermint, both highly concentrated flavourings.

56. Polygonum leaves

These narrow, pointed leaves are also known as Vietnamese mint and *laksa* leaves. They are used for garnishing and flavouring curries. The leaves are either crushed or sliced and used in curries or *laksa*. The leaves are also added to fish dishes to camouflage the fishy smell.

57. Screwpine leaves

Commonly known as *pandan* leaf, the long narrow leaf is used in Singapore, Malaysia, Indonesia and Thailand in savoury dishes and desserts. The leaves, with their delicate flavour, are as essential to Asian cooking as the vanilla essence is to Western cooking. When pounded and strained to extract the juice, the leaves lend flavour and colour to Asian sweets and desserts. They can also be used to wrap marinated meat and other food to add flavour.

58. Spring onions

Spring onions, known as scallions in the United States, have long thin leaves with sometimes a white bulb at the base. Both the white and green portions are chopped and used for garnishing.

59. Torch ginger flower

This bud of the wild ginger flower has a delicate aroma. For cooking purposes, the bud is picked while the petals are still tightly folded. Its intriguing fragrance lends a refreshing aroma to curries and fish dishes. The bud may be eaten raw, where it is finely sliced and added to vegetable salads such as *kerabu* or *rojak*. The full blossom is added to soups and gravies to impart its unique flavour.

60. Turmeric leaf

The leaves of the turmeric plant are very fragrant and used extensively in curries. It is usually shredded to impart a stronger flavour.

FLAVOURING

61, 62. Coconut (whole & grated)

Coconut is indispensable in Malaysian, Singaporean, Indonesian and Thai kitchens. Coconut milk is not the water found in the middle of the coconut; rather it is the liquid extracted from the grated flesh of the coconut. The first extraction is the richest and is called the No.1 milk. Water is then added to the already used coconut flesh and squeezed again to extract a slightly weaker milk referred to as the No.2 milk.

Roasted grated coconut is often added to enrich certain dishes. This is obtained by roasting fresh grated coconut, stirring constantly in a dry pan over low heat until it turns golden brown.

Coconut milk and grated coconut can be found in supermarkets, fresh, canned or powdered, which can then be reconstituted with the addition of water.

63. Kaffir lime

(*See 51. Kaffir lime leaves.*)

64. Kalamansi lime

The juice of this small, round, green citrus fruit is very sour. It adds a tangy flavour to dishes and drinks. It is also referred to as 'local lime'.

65. Lime

This small, lemon-shaped citrus fruit has a thin green skin and a juicy, pale green pulp. Limes grow in tropical and subtropical climes such as Mexico, California, Florida and the Caribbean.

Look for brightly coloured, smooth-skinned limes that are heavy for their size. Small brown areas on the skin won't affect flavour or succulence but a hard or shriveled skin will. Refrigerate uncut limes in a plastic bag for up to 10 days. Cut limes can be stored in the same way up to 5 days. The versatile lime has a multitude of uses, from a sprightly addition to mixed drinks to a marinade for raw fish dishes to the famous desserts.

52

53

54

55

56

57

58

59

60

61

62

63

64

65

OTHER INGREDIENTS ● ● ● ●

66. Almond

Almond is the kernel of the fruit of the almond tree, grown extensively in California, the Mediterranean, Australia and South Africa. There are two main types — sweet and bitter. The flavour of sweet almonds is delicate and slightly sweet. They are readily available in markets and, unless otherwise indicated, are the variety used in recipes. The more strongly flavoured bitter almonds contain traces of lethal prussic acid when raw.

Almonds are available blanched or not, whole, sliced, chopped, candied, smoked, in paste form and in many flavours. Toasting almonds before using in recipes intensifies their flavour and adds crunch.

67. Anchovy, dried

These are salted and sun-dried anchovies. They are available in wet markets and Chinese grocery stores. To store them, remove the head and intestines, rinse quickly and dry thoroughly before storing. Fry them in deep fat when they are dry and they make delicious, crisp snacks that go well with drinks.

68. Black prawn paste

This prawn paste is not to be confused with the dried shrimp paste, or *belacan,* which is more commonly used in Asian cooking. Neither can this be used as a substitute for *belacan.* Black prawn paste (*hay ko* or *petis*) is a black, molasses-like paste made from shrimp, sugar, salt, flour and water. It is most famously used in Penang *laksa.* It is often an acquired taste and has a smoky, earthy pungent flavour.

69. Candlenut

This hard, waxy and beige nut has a slightly bitter taste. Small quantities are pounded or blended into a paste and used as a natural thickener. It also adds a nutty texture and flavour to curry dishes. To prevent it from becoming rancid, store candlenuts in an airtight container in the refrigerator.

70. Char siew

This is lean roasted pork where the surface of the roast has been coloured red. It is often sold alongside roast duck.

71. Chicken stock cube

Chicken stock is obtained by boiling and simmering of chicken bones and carcass for several hours. The stock is strained and refrigerated then its solidified fat that rises on the surface is removed to get a virtually fat-free stock. This stock is then freezed in ice cube trays for future use. Chicken stock is used to give flavours to the dishes.

Ready-made chicken stock cubes can be bought at the supermarkets.

72. Chinese cruellers

These are long fritters of dough which has been deep fried in pairs, so they stick together. In Taiwan, it is eaten for breakfast with soy bean milk. In Singapore and Malaysia, it is often chopped and added to porridge or to *tau suan,* a hot dessert made of green beans. Its name is literally translated to 'oil fried devils', and refers to the fate of a husband-and-wife pair in ancient China who betrayed a well-loved hero.

73. Chinese mushrooms, dried

This is dried shiitake mushrooms and varies in size and price, depending on quality. Soak them in hot water before use. Add the soaking liquid to add to the dish while cooking, or into stocks to lend a richer flavour.

74. Cloud ear fungus

This black fungus should be soaked in water to soften before use. When soaked, it expands into a large, crunchy sheet. With no taste of its own, it offers a crunchy texture and is commonly used in Chinese stir-fries or desserts.

75. Crisp-fried shallots

Crisp-fried shallots are shallots that have been sliced fine and deep-fried in hot cooking oil until golden brown. They are used for flavouring and garnishing. To make them at home, peel the shallots and finely slice them crosswise. Deep-fry in hot oil over low heat, stirring briskly all the while. Turn off the heat as soon as they turn a pale brown. Remove and drain on absorbent paper until cool. Store in an airtight container.

76. Dried prawns

These are sun-dried, salted, steamed prawns. Soak them in water for about 20 minutes to remove excess salt before using. Dried prawns are ground, chopped or left whole and fried to flavour dishes.

77. Dried sour fruit slices

Dried sour fruit (*asam gelugur*) slices is a tangerine-like fruit that is sliced thinly and dried in the sun. Light brown when fresh, it turns darker as it ages. Like tamarind (*asam*), it is used to give acidity to cooked food.

Dried sour fruit slices are usually available from Chinese grocery stores. If not available, substitute with tamarind pulp.

78. Fish maw

Fish maw is the air bladder of the fish. Its main function is to receive and expel huge qualities of water and/or oxygen so that fish can ascend and descend in the water. This makes the bladder very strong and elastic. Dried fish maw is mostly used in the preparation of thick soup. It is effective in relieving coughs and beneficial for the general health.

79. Golden needles

These are the unopened flower buds of orange and yellow day lillies. At certain times of year, you may find fresh lily buds in Asian produce markets, with bright golden petals tightly folded above an emerald green calyx. They are delicious stir-fried with minced pork and flavoured with garlic, black pepper and fish sauce. Lily buds are known as 'golden needles' because of their original colour, though once dried, they fade to a pale brown. Popular with Buddhists and other vegetarians, they add a distinctive, earthy flavour to a dish.

The long, slender dried buds of the day lily (*kim chiam*) are sold in packets and will keep well if stored airtight. Look for buds pale in colour and still flexible, not dark brown and brittle, which indicates they are old. Store in a jar with a tight-fitting lid, away from the light. Before adding to a dish, soak in warm water for 20–30 minutes. Trim soaked buds of hard stem, then either tie each in a knot, shred by tearing, or cut across in halves.

80. Indonesian black nut

Although native to Brazil, this black, hard-shelled nut known locally as *buah keluak,* is grown extensively in Indonesia. The black oily kernel has a slightly bitter taste. A good nut is heavy, does not rattle when shaken and does not produce a hollow sound when tapped lightly.

81. Lime paste

A white substance obtained by burning and grinding cockle shells until fine. It is usually eaten with betel leaves. It is available in some speciality baking stores.

82. Orange peel, dried

Often added to soups and casseroles, it gives a distinct and pleasant orange flavour. The best peel comes from large, brightly coloured fruit. The peel is threaded into twine and dried in the sun for a week. It is often sold in packets and can be bought from most Chinese grocery stores or herbalists. Soak for 20 minutes before use. Keeps indefinitely if stored in an airtight container.

83. Palm sugar

Also known as jaggery, palm sugar is made from the sap of the palm tree. Fresh palm sap is boiled into a concentrated palm syrup, then poured into bamboo sections

66

67

68

69

70

71

72

73

74

75

76

77

78

79

80

81

82

to solidify into cylindrical shapes. Palm sugar, also known as *gula Melaka* or *gula kabung* in Malaysia and *gula Jawa* or *aren* in Indonesia, is used for both savoury dishes and sweets.

84. Peanuts
The nuts have a papery brown skin and are contained in a thin, netted, tan-coloured pod. Peanuts are also called groundnuts or earth nuts because, after flowering, the plant bends down to the earth and buries its pods in the ground. Peanuts are sold unshelled and shelled. The former should have clean, unbroken shells and should not rattle when shaken. Shelled peanuts, often available in vacuum-sealed jars or cans, are usually roasted and sometimes salted. Refrigerate unshelled peanuts tightly wrapped for up to 6 months.

85. *Poh pia* skin
These are large, tissue-thin skins of rice flour dough which are used for making spring rolls. They are sold in packets of 25 or 50, and if frozen, should be thoroughly thawed before using. They are becoming widely

available in supermarkets, though some specialty artisans still make them fresh and continue to be in great demand among *poh pia* aficionados. Keep unused wrappers in plastic wrap or covered with a damp cloth until ready to use; once they have dried out, they break easily and become impossible to fold.

86. Preserved Tientsin cabbage
This brownish-green pieces of the stem of the Chinese cabbage that has been preserved in brine (*tung chye*). It has a savoury, mildly salty flavour and a firm, crisp texture. Sold in jars, it can be bought from Oriental markets. Rinse thoroughly before use.

87. Processed cuttlefish
The cuttlefish, which resembles a rather large squid, has 10 appendages and can reach up to 6.5 metres in length. It can be prepared like its less tender relatives, the squid and octopus, but must still be tenderized before cooking in order not to be exceedingly chewy. Cuttlefish are most popular in Japan, India and many Mediterranean

countries. Dried cuttlefish is available in some Asian markets. It should be reconstituted before cooking. To reconstitute, soak in warm water for several hours, then simmer in clean water.

88. Red beans
Also known as adzuki or aduki beans, red beans are usually cooked during celebrations in China and Japan because red is considered an auspicious and lucky colour. The beans are usually boiled with sugar and mashed to make fillings for sweet cakes or sweet soups.

89. Salted fish, Penang
Dried and salted fish are a Malaysian speciality. Highly flavourful, it is used in small amounts in curries and sambals. It is also added to stir fries to lift an otherwise bland dish.

90. Salted radish
This is finely diced radish preserved in spices and salt to get golden-brown morsels that are crisp and eaten as a relish (*chai poh*). There is also another type known in Chinese as *tai tou choy*. The latter is made from whole radish cut into slices

lengthwise and with all the leaves intact, salted and dried.

91. Sesame seeds
Native to India, sesame seeds have a strong, pleasant, nutty flavour and are frequently used in breads, salads and to make oil. They are available in black and white varieties.

92. Shrimp paste
Dried shrimp paste is made from small shrimps, which have been dried in the sun before being pounded into a paste. This strong smelling condiment is widely used in Malay and Nyonya cooking. It is pounded and blended with other spices and seasonings to make a spice mix which is the base for *sambal* dishes, curries and spicy gravies. Dried shrimp paste can be bought fresh whole or as pre-roasted granules.

93. Sugared winter melon
This is winter melon crystallised in sugar (*tung kwa*). Often sold in the dried foods section of a Chinese grocery or supermarket, it is used in various Chinese desserts (*tong soi*) and home made barley water.

94. Tamarind pulp
The tamarind fruit or *asam*, is commonly used in Southeast Asian cooking. The long pods contain pulp-covered seeds, which are usually dried and sold. This pulp is soaked in water for about 10 minutes and strained of any fibres and seeds. The sour juice is used, and adds fragrance and flavour to dishes.

95. Wheat
Wheat is the world's largest cereal-grass crop. Its status as a staple is second only to rice. Wheat contains a relatively high amount of gluten, the protein that provides the elasticity necessary for excellent breadmaking. Though there are over 30,000 varieties, the three major types are hard wheat, soft wheat and durum wheat.

96. Yellow bean paste
Popular in Nyonya cooking, this light brown paste is made of preserved soy beans, and lends an earthy, salty flavour to dishes. A variation of this paste incorporates chilli and is sold as spicy bean paste.

83

84

85

86

87

88

89

90

91

92

93

94

95

96

97. Bean curd (firm and soft)
Firm bean curd (*taukwa*) is pressed and quite heavy. It is the firmest bean curd of all and very versatile.

Soft bean curd is available in slabs from the wet market or in rectangular containers and tubes from the supermarket. It has the texture of custard. Handle carefully to prevent breaking it. There are several varieties of bean curd including silken bean curd and cotton bean curd which is slightly firmer, but not as firm as *taukwa*. It is also available combined with egg, and sold as 'egg bean curd'. These are often cylindrical in shape and sport a distinctive yellow shade.

98. Bean curd puffs
Known as *taupok*, these are deep-fried bean curd puffs, which are either round or square in shape. They are light, with a golden brown exterior and a soft, somewhat 'honeycomb' interior. Whether it is stuffed with fish or meat, or is eaten as it is, it has an easy to chew texture, which gives it a very distinctive taste. Like all bean curd, it absorbs other flavours well.

99, 100. Bean curd skin and sticks
Dried bean curd skin can be found in stick and strips (*foo chok*) or sheets (*foo pei*). This comes from the thin, yellow layer that forms on the surface of soy bean milk before it coagulates. *Foo chok* is commonly used in desserts. *Foo pei* comes in sheets about 60-cm wide. They are sold folded like plastic sheets and are available at stores selling bean curd, Chinese grocery stores and supermarkets. Do not refrigerate them.

101. Sweet bean curd strips (*tim chok*)
These are small, seasoned, brown rectangular pieces of dried bean curd known as *tim chok*. These are used mainly in vegetarian cooking.

102. Cellophane noodles
The vermicelli-like noodles are made from mung bean flour. They are also called glass noodles or bean starch noodles. They should be soaked in water before being added to boiling soups or stir-fried vegetables. Cellophane noodles are used in Japanese, Thai Burmese, Vietnamese, Chinese, Malaysian, Philippine and Indonesian cooking.

103. Coarse rice vermicelli, fresh
Made from rice flour, these *laksa* noodles are as thick as spaghetti. Dried rice vermicelli can be used as a substitute if fresh noodles are not available.

104. Fine wheat vermicelli
These Filipino off-white dried wheat noodles (*mee suah*) are very slender. They can be deep-fried to make a crunchy nest or boiled for 2–3 minutes to make a salad or be added directly to soup.

105. Rice noodles
Made from rice flour, these flat, opaque noodles (*kway teow*) are about 1-cm ($1/2$-in) wide. They are available fresh or dried and can be boiled or fried. Dried noodles should be soaked for up to 30 minutes to soften.

106. Rice vermicelli
Rice vermicelli (*bee hoon*) is made from rice flour. It can be fried or cooked in a soup. The dried variety needs to be soaked first in cold or hot water to soften, then drained, before cooking.

107. Yellow egg noodles
These large, yellow noodles are made of wheat and are either round (often called Hokkien noodles) or slightly flattened (*mee pok*). They should be rinsed and drained thoroughly before being fried. Like all fresh noodles, they should not be kept for more than a day before using, otherwise they tend to become heavy.

108. Banana leaf
Used in almost every Asian country, the banana leaf is often shaped into cones, square containers, neat rectangular packages to be used as wrappers, or to take the place of a plate. When used as a plate, the mid-rib of the leaf is retained. As a wrapper, the mid-rib is removed. Before shaping it, blanch the banana leaf in boiling water briefly to render it pliable.

97

98

99

100

101

102

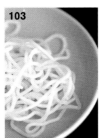
103

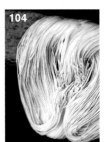
104

105

106

107

108

INDEX TO THE GLOSSARY OF INGREDIENTS